Finding Your Math Power

CONCEPTS IN MATHEMATICS FOR ELEMENTARY SCHOOL TEACHERS

By Karla Karstens

FIRST EDITION

cognella® | ACADEMIC PUBLISHING

Bassim Hamadeh, CEO and Publisher

Kassie Graves, Director of Acquisitions

Jamie Giganti, Senior Managing Editor

Miguel Macias, Senior Graphic Designer

John Remington, Senior Field Acquisitions Editor

Monika Dziamka, Project Editor

Brian Fahey, Licensing Specialist

Allie Kiekhofer and Claire Yee, Interior Designers

Cover image copyright© by Depositphotos / poznyakov.

copyright © by Depositphotos / Elinacious.

Printed in the United States of America

ISBN: 978-1-63487-195-2 (pbk) / 978-1-63487-196-9 (br) / 978-1-63487-530-1 (pf)

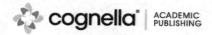

Contents

DEDICATION

This book is dedicated to Mr. David Dooley, who inspired me to become a teacher, and Mr. James DeMorritt, who shared his love of math with many at Cooper High School.

Special thanks to Sandy, Bethany, and Will—my wonderful family—and Joe Kudrle, who was always willing to help.

To the Student

This is not a formal math book, but it is an important math book. It is important because it celebrates your transition from math student to math teacher. As a math student, getting the answer was usually the most important, if not the only important, part of a math problem. As a future math teacher, this book will help you realize that there is much more to a math problem than the answer. How did you get the answer? Can you find the answer another way? What does the answer mean? Can you connect this problem to another problem you've done that is similar in nature? Why does the answer to the problem make sense? All of these questions will become more important to you as you progress through your studies to become a math educator—one of the most rewarding and challenging jobs I know!

This math book assumes basic knowledge about operations on Real numbers and should be thought of as a user's manual. The focus is on expanding your repertoire of ways to work with whole numbers, fractions, decimals, percent, and integers, with many examples and practice problems included. Some ideas may be new and others may be familiar to you but presented a bit differently. You may already know a lot of math, but as a teacher, you need to have a broad base of knowledge. One way to work out a problem is rarely enough. You want to have more than one way to approach a problem to meet the many and varied needs of your students.

Some of you may be very comfortable with mathematical ideas and others may have moments of math anxiety. This book is meant to be encouraging and inspiring. Use it as a guide to the Real Number System and bring out the proud and fearless math guru that lives in every one of us. Your goal is to find your own MATH POWER and see where it takes you—have fun!

"It is impossible to overstate the importance of problem solving in mathematics. It is by means of problems that mathematics develops and actually lifts itself by its own bootstraps . . . Every new discovery in mathematics, results from an attempt to solve some problem."

—Howard Eves

CHAPTER 1

Problem Solving

In this chapter, you will begin anew your study of mathematics. This time, you are looking at math through the lens of a future teacher as well as a student.

 Math Power Goals:
- Learn the steps for effective problem solving.
- Push yourself to go beyond finding the answer to a problem by verifying the solution or using a different method to solve the problem.

A History of Math Education and Current Standards

Welcome, and congratulations! You've undertaken the wonderful task of becoming a teacher.

Susan Fuhrman, in an article for *USA Weekend*, points out teachers and presidents have similar and important occupations. Each endeavor requires many of the same skills. You need to excel at answering to a large and varied audience, be able to think on your feet, be open to new information, and be able to collaborate with others. Additionally, you must be a role model and instill basic rules of good behavior in others. Everything you do in the classroom makes a difference in your students' lives, though often you, and they, don't realize it until a later time.

You will only be successful if your students receive your message, and in order to do this, you need to build connections. The ability to create relationships with your students is probably one of the hardest things to do as a teacher, but it is also the most rewarding aspect of the job.

The best way to start making those relationships with your students is to be comfortable and confident in all of the subjects you will be teaching, including the subject of this book—MATHEMATICS. What is mathematics? More than arithmetic, mathematics can be thought of as the science of pattern and order that helps us interpret the world around us. A person uses mathematical observations to identify regularity, suggest logical conjectures, test predictions, and draw reasoned conclusions. It is the language and backbone of science and technology.

This course, an overview of the math you've learned with a focus on developing broader approaches and new strategies, is the first step toward increasing your numeracy skills. Being numerate is more than being able to add, subtract, multiply, and divide; it's the ability to cope confidently with the mathematical demands of adult life.

A Brief History of Math Teaching

About sixty years ago, on October 4, 1957, the Soviets launched Sputnik I into space. This event initiated a "Space Race" with Russia. President John F. Kennedy challenged our country to land a man on the moon, a grand and ambitious goal. The perception was that in order to achieve this amazing goal, our math curriculum needed to change. As a result, a team of mathematicians created what was called "New Math." Math didn't change, but new topics, such as sets, were brought to the forefront. Teachers received very little training in the New Math, and they, as well as parents, were discouraged. In 1969, Neil Armstrong landed on the moon, and the need for New Math faded into the background.

What took its place was a pendulum swing in the other direction. New Math was replaced by the "Back to the Basics" movement, with a focus on skills and testing. Then, in 1983, the paper "A Nation at Risk" exposed the gap between the United States and Japan in mathematical ability, which led to math curriculums leaning more heavily on critical thinking and word problems. In 1989, the National Council of Teachers of Mathematics (NCTM) published *Curriculum and Evaluation Standards of School Mathematics*. The Standards emphasized processing skills, which some perceived to mean that computation was not important, and included evaluation standards. It was well-received in isolated pockets, but it was not enough to influence change. Then, after a less than positive report from TIMSS (The Third International Math and Science Study) in 1996 and NAEP (National Assessment of Educational Progress) in 2000, things started looking up in April 2000, when NCTM published *Principles and Standards for School Mathematics*.

The NCTM Principles and Standards gave teachers a roadmap that would lead to a better math education for their students. Objectives and ideas were presented in groups of five and were a guide rather than a to-do list. This allowed teachers to be flexible and creative while also being aware of the aims of the curriculum.

The Principles and Standards lists five Student Goals:

- Learn to value math.

- Become confident in their ability to do math.

- Become mathematical problem solvers.

- Learn to communicate mathematics.

- Learn to reason mathematically.

The Principles and Standards also lists five Content Standards (what you need to learn) and five Process Standards (how you will learn):

Content Standards

- Number and Operations

- Algebra

- Geometry

- Measurement

- Data Analysis and Probability

Process Standards

- Problem Solving

- Reasoning and Proof

- Communication

- Connections

- Representation

Finally, the most important part of the document speaks to the five shifts in the classroom environment.

- Toward classrooms as mathematical communities and away from classrooms as simply a collection of individuals.

- Toward logic and mathematical evidence as verification and away from the teacher as the sole authority for right answers.

- Toward mathematical reasoning and away from mere memorizing procedures (rules).

- Toward conjecturing, inventing, and problem solving and away from an emphasis on mechanistic finding of answers.

- Toward connecting mathematics, its ideas, and its applications and away from treating mathematics as a body of isolated concepts and procedures.

The goal behind the changes was to create skillful math students who are also adept at problem solving and excited and interested in mathematics. The same is true for the math educator. In order to be successful as a math teacher, you need to be open to new ways of thinking about mathematics. Being a math educator is different than being a math student. In order to be the best math teacher you can be, you need to have mental preparation, a solid knowledge of mathematics, persistence, a positive attitude, readiness for change, and self-reflection. All of these aspects will be developed and broadened during the course of the semester as you work to find and increase your own personal MATH POWER!

Ready to accept the challenge of increasing your Math Power? Wonderful, because that is the goal of this course. To achieve this goal, we'll be using a constructive, problem-solving approach. With constructivism, students create their own meaning and understanding of mathematics through experience, often incorporating a variety of techniques (hands-on, visual, kinesthetic, etc.). Interacting with the math through problem solving and reflecting and looking back on what they learned will be the common thread throughout the course.

Here is a problem that seems impossible, but isn't, a great way to start your math journey. To solve this problem, the first step is the hardest—do SOMETHING. Once you get started (even if it is only guess and check, a very acceptable problem-solving strategy), your efforts may not get you the correct solution right away, but they will give you some information that should get you closer to the answer. Keep at it. As you continue, you will be able to zero in until you find the answer. The best part is that once you have the solution, you will KNOW that it is correct. Then you experience the same joy quarterbacks feel when they throw a completed pass, spellers feel when they spell a word correctly, and designers feel when they watch their dress on the runway—I DID IT!

The Egg Problem

Jay has some eggs to sell, and Kay, May, and Ray want to buy them. Jay sells half the eggs plus half an egg to Kay, then sells half the remaining eggs plus half an egg to May, and finally sells half the remaining eggs plus half an egg to Ray. At the end of the three sales, Jay is out of eggs. The strange thing is that Jay never had to break an egg. How many eggs did Jay have to sell?

1.1 First Day Reflection

What Do You Think?

1. List five qualities of a good math student below:

2. List five qualities of a good math teacher below:

3. What does MATH POWER mean to you?

4. List two goals for the semester. What are you going to do to increase your MATH POWER?

Problem Solving

To have a section titled "Problem Solving" is rather deceiving because this entire course is problem solving in some way, shape, or form. However, it is customary in a course such as this to start by presenting techniques of problem solving and have students work through some problems in order to get their math gears going. It's a good way to start the course, and it helps to emphasize that problem solving is the common thread throughout the course and the context in which the math is presented.

George Polya and Problem Solving

George Polya has been called "The Father of Problem Solving," and in the book *How to Solve It*, published in 1945, he outlined techniques for solving problems. I have found that people have a very personal approach to problem solving, but Polya's steps are a good place to start, and they provide a nice foundation that is often useful.

Step 1: Understand the Problem

Do you know the meaning of the words, and do you understand the context of the problem?

Do you know what you are trying to find? What type of solution are you looking for?

Step 2: Devise a Plan

Have you seen this problem before? Is this problem similar to something you've solved previously?

How will you start to solve this problem? What strategies might you use?

- Guess and check

- Make a list

- Look for a pattern

- Solve a simpler problem

- Work backward

- Draw a picture or diagram

Step 3: Carry Out the Plan

Execute the strategy you adopted in step 2. This is the step where you calculate, count, evaluate, or solve to find a solution.

Step 4: Look Back

This step is often overlooked, but it is very important. Check your solution and see that it is complete and correct. Is your answer labeled properly? Have you answered the question stated in the problem, or do you have more work to do? Think about your problem-solving process and evaluate its effectiveness. Now that you have a solution, is there another method that might have worked better?

All right, now we have some ideas, so let's solve some problems and see how the process works. In other books, the problems are generally grouped by problem-solving strategy, but I don't think that's the most effective way to become a good problem solver. Besides, I may think the best way to solve a particular problem would be to make a list, while you may think guess and check is the best approach. The most important thing is to do SOMETHING to start the problem-solving process, not which method you use. So be open-minded as you work through these problems. I will try to present the solution in a number of different ways to illustrate that the best way to solve a problem is the method YOU used to get a solution! But once you've solved a problem, it might be helpful to see other ways to find an answer so you can broaden your problem-solving skills.

EXAMPLE 1.2.1 Drew's Sport Shop

Drew sells bicycles and tricycles at his Sport Shop. One morning, he was looking at his bike display and said, "I count 16 handlebars and 38 wheels." How many bicycles and how many tricycles does Drew have on display in his shop?

Step 1: Understand the Problem

Think about this problem and some of the important details you need to answer the question. Some thoughts might be "a bicycle has two wheels and a tricycle has three wheels" and "there are 16 handlebars, so there must be 16 cycles in all." My answer will be the number of bicycles and the number of tricycles, and my answer should add up to 16.

Here are some ways to solve the problem.

SOLUTION 1

Step 2: Devise a Plan—Use a Formula (Algebraically)

Let b = the number of bicycles and t = the number of tricycles and create two equations, one for the number of handlebars and one for the number of wheels.

Step 3: Carry Out the Plan

Together, the equations are $\begin{array}{l} b+t=16 \\ 2b+3t=38 \end{array}$ and the solution of this system of equations will result in $b = 10$ and $t = 6$.

So the answer would be 10 bicycles and 6 tricycles.

Step 4: Look Back

Checking the answer, you can see that $10 + 6 = 16$, so the number of handlebars is correct, and $2(10) + 3(6) = 20 + 18 = 38$, so the number of wheels is correct. Looks like 10 bicycles and 6 tricycles is the solution. Great problem solving!

Even though you were able to solve the problem, using algebra to solve this type of problem is not very practical when teaching elementary school children. If you think the only way to solve this problem is to use algebra, you couldn't introduce this type of question in an elementary classroom. Are there other ways to solve the problem that would be more appropriate for elementary school children? This is the approach that I hope you take as we continue. You've been exposed to a lot of math in your lifetime so far, but with this book, I hope you will look at problem solving through the eyes of a younger child who is seeing problems like this for the first time. Connecting with your inner math child is a good approach for this class.

Something else to consider is that finding a solution is only one part of the problem-solving process. As a student, that was probably your only goal. As a teacher looking to build a firm foundation in problem solving, you want to spend more time on the looking back step. Talking to others in the class who solved the problem a different way will increase your own Math Power and help you realize not all people see things the way you do. We are individual in our approaches, but in a classroom, you will have to find a way to connect with each child and his or her unique math background. Having more tools at your disposal makes you a better teacher and gives your students more ideas to work with.

SOLUTION 2

Step 2: Devise a Plan—Guess and Check

I'm going to guess that half of the display is bicycles and half is tricycles.

Step 3: Carry Out the Plan

If half the display is bicycles and half is tricycles, and knowing that there are 16 cycles in all, then 8 will be bicycles and 8 will be tricycles.

This means there will be 8(2) = 16 bicycle wheels and 8(3) = 24 tricycle wheels or 40 wheels, which is too many wheels.

Adjusting my numbers by turning one tricycle into a bicycle, I now have 9 bicycles and 7 tricycles. This means there will be 9(2) = 18 bicycle wheels and 7(3) = 21 tricycle wheels or 39 wheels, which is still too high. Changing another tricycle into a bicycle results in 10 bicycles and 6 tricycles, which means there will be 10(2) = 20 bicycle wheels and 6(3) = 18 tricycle wheels, which gives a total of 38 wheels—the right number. That's the solution!

SOLUTION 3

Step 2: Devise a Plan—Make a Table

Step 3: Carry Out the Plan

Number of Bicycles	Number of Bicycle Wheels	Number of Tricycles	Number of Tricycle Wheels	Total Number of Wheels
1	2	15	45	47
2	4	14	42	46
3	6	13	39	45
4	8	12	36	44
5	10	11	33	43
6	12	10	30	42
7	14	9	27	41
8	16	8	24	40
9	18	7	21	39
10	20	6	18	38* Solution!

One benefit of making the table is that you can see patterns. Sometimes students think that if they have one more tricycle, they will gain three more wheels. At each change, the number of cycles stays the same, so having one more tricycle means you change a bicycle into a tricycle, with an overall change of only one wheel added to the total. If students recognize this pattern, they may be able to find the solution to the problem by making a large jump rather than increasing the number of tricycles by one each time.

SOLUTION 4

Step 2: Devise a Plan—Draw a Picture

Step 3: Carry Out the Plan

We know there are 16 handlebars, so draw one for each cycle:

Now, let's assume each cycle is a bicycle and draw two wheels for each handlebar:

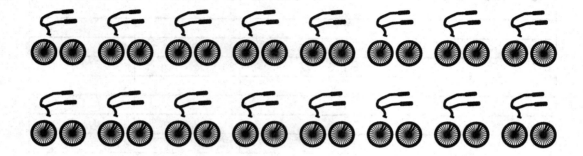

Counting the number of wheels you get 32, which is 6 fewer than needed for the answer. We need more wheels, but we can easily turn a bicycle into a tricycle by adding another wheel. If we count by 1s as we go, we can see that changing 6 bicycles into tricycles will give us 10 bicycles and 6 tricycles with a total of 38 wheels, which is the correct answer.

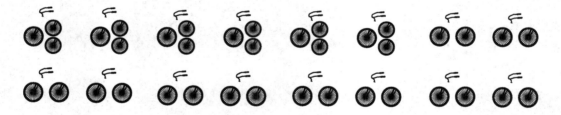

This solution is brilliant in its simplicity. The best part is that even young children should be able to connect with the process of finding the answer and be able to explain it in a way that makes sense to others who listen.

One positive and empowering aspect of problem solving is that if you make a habit of looking back and checking your solution, you will <u>know</u> that you have the right answer. You don't need to have your teacher or a friend tell you that your answer is correct; you <u>know</u> it is. There is an amazing feeling of satisfaction when you solve a problem and you know you have the correct solution!

EXAMPLE 1.2.2 Getting to Know You!

There are 10 people in a Math 15 classroom. If each person shakes hands with everyone in the classroom, how many handshakes are needed? (Note: Ann shaking hands with Betty is the same as Betty shaking hands with Ann and counts as one handshake.)

Step 1: Understand the Problem

The note is a helpful clarification in terms of understanding the problem. You need to know how to count handshakes. Another observation is that you don't shake hands with yourself! The answer to this problem will be the number of handshakes.

Here are some different approaches to solving this problem.

SOLUTION 1

Step 2: Make a List

I'm going to think of the 10 people as A, B, C, D, E, F, G, H, I, and J.

I'll list the handshakes A makes and then B and continue through all the people in the class.

Step 3: Carry Out the Plan

AB	BC	CD	DE	EF	FG	GH	HI	IJ
AC	BD	CE	DF	EG	FH	GI	IJ	
AD	BE	CF	DG	EH	FI	GJ		
AE	BF	CG	DH	EI	FJ			
AF	BG	CH	DI	EJ				
AG	BH	CI	DJ					
AH	BI	CJ						
AI	BJ							
AJ								

9	8	7	6	5	4	3	2	1

The total number would be 9 + 8 + 7 + 6 + 5 + 4 + 3 + 2 + 1 = 45 handshakes.

Step 4: Looking Back

As you work out this problem, you may see that there is a pattern with the number of handshakes as you move through the group. Each person shakes hands with one less classmate than the previous person. With 10 people in the class, we have $9 + 8 + 7 + 6 + 5 + 4 + 3 + 2 + 1 = 45$, and we can project that if the class had 7 people, the total number of handshakes would be $6 + 5 + 4 + 3 + 2 + 1 = 21$ handshakes. Similarly, if there were 50 people in the class, you would add $49 + 48 + 47 + \ldots + 3 + 2 + 1 = 1{,}225$ handshakes.

SOLUTION 2

Step 2: Draw a Picture or Diagram

Represent each person with a circle and draw a line between circles to represent handshakes.

Step 3: Carry Out the Plan.

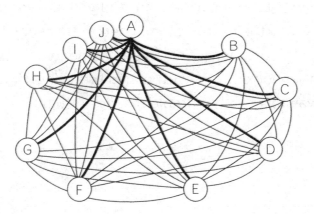

Each person has 9 lines coming out of his or her circle, but those lines are the "double counts" because A shaking with B and B shaking with A are both represented.

To find the correct number of handshakes, you would have 10 (people) x 9 (handshakes) = 90 handshakes. Then divide this number by 2 because of the double counting.

So there would be $\frac{10(9)}{2} = 45$ handshakes.

Step 4: Looking Back

The method could also be generalized in that if you have 20 people, you would have $\frac{20(19)}{2} = 190$ handshakes. In fact, if you have n people, you would have $\frac{n(n-1)}{2}$ handshakes.

This is just a taste of problem solving, and you'll have the opportunity to practice more with the exercises included in this section and then later at the end of the book. Your first goal should be to get started, then solve the problem, then look back—with bonus brownie points awarded if you see another way to solve the problem successfully. Have fun!

1.2 Problem Set

1. Right now, Jason is 5 and his father is 29 years old. How old will Jason be when Jason's father's age is three times Jason's age?

2. Mr. and Mrs. Hesslink want to put a fence around their 4-sided garden. They have 40 feet of fencing. What dimensions will maximize the area of the garden?

3. Consider the following addition problem:

$$
\begin{array}{r}
E\ L\ F \\
+\ E\ L\ F \\
\hline
F\ O\ O\ L
\end{array}
$$

   Each letter represents a unique nonzero number. Find the value of each letter so the problem makes sense mathematically.

4. Larry, Moe, and Curly have 5 pies. If each one of them is to get at least one pie, how many ways can they be distributed so there are none left over? The pies cannot be cut up and must remain whole.

5. The Parpart family has 6 members. They are renting three tandem bikes to explore Stowe, Vermont. Each member of the family wants to have a turn to ride with each other member of the family for a day. How many days will they need for their exploring if all 6 family members go out together each day?

6. Mrs. Schoales was happy to see so many students in the school band who turned out for the parade. She had them form rows of 5, but it turned out that just one tuba player was in the back row. To her dismay, when she tried to reform the band into rows of 4, there was still a lone tuba player in the back row. In desperation, Mrs. Schoales had the band reassemble into rows of 9. To her relief, every row was filled with no one left over! How many students were in the parade band?

7. How many different ways can you make 50 cents using only quarters, dimes, nickels, and pennies?

8. Ms. Puterbaugh's class has 12 students. How many different ways can you have a class president, vice president, and secretary if no person can hold more than one position?

9. Find the number that best completes the following sequence.

    1   2   4   7   11   16   ?   29

10. Connor bought 4 stickers and 3 bouncy balls for 90 cents. The next day, he bought 3 stickers and 4 bouncy balls for 85 cents. How much did each sticker and bouncy ball cost?

11. Farmer Barton has 21 baskets of apples: 7 full, 7 half full, and 7 empty. He wants to divide them equally among his 3 children. How can he do this—without transferring any portion of the apples from basket to basket—so that each child will have not only an equal quantity of apples, but also an equal number of baskets?

12. Jenn has red flowers with 5 petals each and white flowers with 8 petals each. She has a total of 9 flowers with 54 petals. How many red flowers and white flowers are there?

13. A quiz has 18 problems. The total point value of the quiz is 66 points. If each multiple-choice problem is worth 5 points and each true-false problem is worth 3 points, how many of each kind of problem does the quiz have?

14. A family has 4 children: Freeda, Hakeem, Lani, and Susan. Susan is younger than Lani. Hakeem is older than Lani. Freeda is younger than Hakeem but older than Lani. List the children in order from youngest to oldest.

15. A carpenter has 8 separate large boxes. Inside each large box are 2 medium-size boxes. Inside each medium-size box are 5 separate small boxes. How many boxes (of all sizes) are there altogether?

1.2 Solutions

1. When Jason is 12, his dad will be three times his age, or 36 years old.

2. The maximum area of a "rectangular" garden is 10 feet by 10 feet. (Note: A square is a rectangle.)

3. F = 1, E = 7, L = 2, O = 4

4. 6 different ways:

	Larry	Moe	Curly	
	1	1	3	pies
	1	3	1	pies
	3	1	1	pies
	2	2	1	pies
	2	1	2	pies
	1	2	2	pies

5. 5 days

Think of the family members as A, B, C, D, E, F

Day 1	AB	CD	EF
Day 2	AC	BE	DF
Day 3	AD	BF	CE
Day 4	AE	BD	CF
Day 5	AF	BC	DE

6. 81 students in the band

7. 45 ways

Q	2	1	1	1	1	1	1	1	1	0	0	0	0	0	0	0	0	0	0	0	0	0	0	0	0
D	0	2	2	1	1	1	1	0	0	5	4	4	4	3	3	3	3	3	2	2	2	2	2	2	2
N	0	1	0	3	2	1	0	1	0	0	2	1	0	4	3	2	1	0	6	5	4	3	2	1	0
P	0	0	5	0	5	10	15	20	25	0	0	5	10	0	5	10	15	20	0	5	10	15	20	25	30

Q	0	0	0	0	0	0	0	0	0	0	0	0	0	0	0	0	0	0	0	0
D	1	1	1	1	1	1	1	1	1	0	0	0	0	0	0	0	0	0	0	0
N	8	7	6	5	4	3	2	1	0	10	9	8	7	6	5	4	3	2	1	0
P	0	5	10	15	20	25	30	35	40	0	5	10	15	20	25	30	35	40	45	50

8. 1,320 different ways

9. Missing digit is 22: 1, 2, 4, 7, 11, 16, 22, 29 (Note: to get the second number in the sequence add 1, then add 2 to get the next, then 3 for the next, etc.)

10. Stickers are 15 cents and bouncy balls are 10 cents.

11. Child 1 would get 2 full baskets, 3 half-full baskets, and 2 empty baskets
    Child 2 would get 3 full baskets, 1 half-full basket, and 3 empty baskets
    Child 3 would get 2 full baskets, 3 half-full baskets, and 2 empty baskets

12. 6 red flowers and 3 white flowers

13. 6 multiple-choice questions and 12 true-false questions

14. Susan, Lani, Freeda, then Hakeem

15. 104 boxes

Image Credits

Section 1.2

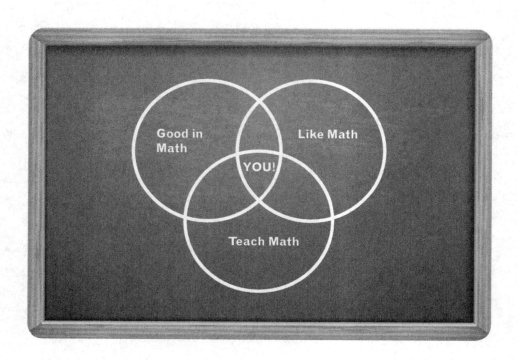

CHAPTER 2

Sets and Venn Diagrams

In this chapter, you will learn that math is more than numbers. It is a way of making connections and learning how to categorize objects.

Math Power Goals:

- Learn the difference between the intersection of two or more sets and the union of two or more sets.
- Understand how Venn diagrams show relationships between sets.
- Identify regions represented in Venn diagrams.

Sets and Set Operations

Mathematics is as much about language and definitions as it is about numbers. A nice place to start when discussing mathematics is with sets and set operations.

What is a set? A set is a well-defined collection of objects or elements. What does it mean to be well-defined? If a set definition is well-defined, then you know exactly whether something should or shouldn't be in the set. The set "Academy Award-Winning Movies" is well-defined. You could look on the Academy Award website and see the movies that are listed. The set "tall people" is not well-defined. A certain person may seem tall to a toddler, but not tall to a WNBA basketball player.

Sets are usually described in one of two ways: as a list (or roster) or as a rule (or definition). Sets are represented using capital letters. Here are some examples:

Rule $L = \{$The Great Lakes of the United States$\}$
Roster $L = \{$Lake Huron, Lake Ontario, Lake Michigan, Lake Erie, Lake Superior$\}$

Rule $E = \{$Even whole numbers$\}$

Roster $E = \{0, 2, 4, 6, 8, 10, \ldots \}$

Symbols are very helpful in the language of sets. The symbol $\in$ means "is an element of" a set, and $\notin$ means "is not an element of" a set. Just like in the movie *Ghostbusters*, the slash means "not." If $F = \{1,2,3,4,5\}$ then $3 \in F$ and $9 \notin F$.

Some sets, such as L, are finite, meaning you can count the number of elements in the set. Other sets, such as E, are infinite sets. The elements in set E continue without ending. Another important set is the Null Set or Empty Set. The Null Set is the set with no elements. It is represented by $\emptyset$. One example of the Null Set is $M = \{$Multiples of 5 that end with the number 7$\}$. Since all multiples of 5 end in either 0 or 5, this set represents the Null Set. The Universal Set is the set of all elements under consideration in a situation. The Universal Set is generally large, such as the whole numbers or all the citizens in the United States. The Universal Set is represented by U.

Venn diagrams are very helpful when visualizing sets. Generally, the Universal Set is represented by a rectangle and sets are shown by circles, ovals, and other shapes. This Venn diagram shows the relationships between sets A, B, and C.

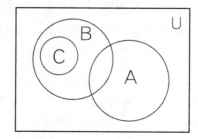

Operations on sets

Sets are especially interesting when there are two or more to consider. When this happens, it is possible to talk mathematically about relationships between the sets. The most common relationships are the intersection and union of two or more sets, the complement of a set, and the idea of a subset, or a set within a set.

Intersection

The intersection of two sets A and B, written $A \cap B$, is the set of elements in set A and in set B. The intersection is represented visually by the Venn diagram below:

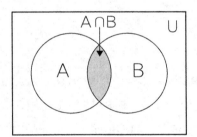

The idea of the intersection of two sets follows intuitively from the idea of the word "intersection" in everyday situations. An intersection in a town is the place where two roads cross. The intersection, where the roads cross, is technically part of both roads. The intersection of two sets is those elements that are in both sets. When considering the intersection between two sets, most people think of the word AND. Your students may need a bit more explanation, so it is helpful to have different words to use when talking about the intersection between two sets.

Other words that are helpful when thinking about the intersection of two sets are OVERLAP, IN COMMON, and BOTH.

EXAMPLE 2.1.1

Let $N = \{n, u, m, b, e, r\}$ $M = \{m, o, n, e, y\}$ $B = \{b, o, u, n, c, e\}$
a. List the elements in $N \cap M$
b. List the elements in $N \cap B$
c. List the elements in $M \cap B$
d. List the elements in $N \cap M \cap B$

SOLUTION

    a. $\{n, m, e\}$ b. $\{n, u, b, e\}$ c. $\{o, n, e\}$ d. $\{n, e\}$

UNION

The union of two sets A and B, written $A \cup B$, is the set of elements in set A or in set B or in both sets A and B. The intersection is represented visually by the Venn diagram below:

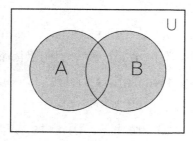

When I think about the union of two sets, I think about a couple getting married, a union of two people. The union brings together people who are from each spouse's side, along with the couple, who are now members of both families. The word most commonly associated with the union of two sets is OR. The union of two sets is the elements in one set OR the other set OR in both sets. If students need other ways to think about the union, consider using COMBINE, BRING TOGETHER, or JOIN TOGETHER. When finding the union of two sets, the best way to proceed is to start with one of the sets and then add the elements of the other set that aren't already in the first set.

EXAMPLE 2.1.2

Let $N = \{n, u, m, b, e, r\}$ $M = \{m, o, n, e, y\}$ $B = \{b, o, u, n, c, e\}$

a. List the elements in $N \cup M$

b. List the elements in $N \cup B$

c. List the elements in $M \cup B$

d. List the elements in $N \cup M \cup B$

SOLUTION

a. $\{n, u, m, b, e, r, o, y\}$

b. $\{n, u, m, b, e, r, o, c\}$

c. $\{m, o, n, e, y, b, u, c\}$

d. $\{n, u, m, b, e, r, o, y, c\}$

Students often get the intersection and the union mixed up. One thing to remember is that the intersection is usually a smaller set and the union is a larger set.

Complement

The complement A, written A', is the set of elements in the Universal set that are not in set A. The complement is represented visually in the Venn diagram:

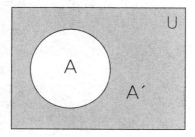

When considering the complement of a set, the word used most often is NOT. Other words to describe the complement include OPPOSITE or EVERYTHING ELSE BUT.

The set A and its complement, A', are what are known as mutually exclusive sets. Sets that are mutually exclusive have no elements in common. The intersection between two mutually exclusive sets is the Null Set or Empty Set, ∅.

Be careful when thinking about the complement of a set. The complement of the set of even numbers is the set of odd numbers because every number is either even or odd. The complement of the set of Republicans is not the set of Democrats, since there are a number of other political parties that are not Republican, such as Independents, Libertarians, etc. The complement of Republicans would be non-Republicans.

EXAMPLE 2.1.3

Let $U = \{1, 2, 3, 4, 5, 6, 7, 8\}$ $A = \{1, 2, 3\}$ $B = \{6, 7, 8\}$ $C = \{2, 4, 6, 8\}$

a. List the elements in A'

b. List the elements in B'

c. List the elements in C'

d. List the elements in $A' \cup C$

e. List the elements in $A' \cap C$

f. List the elements in $A' \cap B'$

g. List the elements in $(A \cap B)'$

B SOLUTION

a. $A' = \{4, 5, 6, 7, 8\}$ b. $B' = \{1, 2, 3, 4, 5\}$ c. $C' = \{1, 3, 5, 7\}$

d. $A' \cup C = \{4, 5, 6, 7, 8, 2\}$

e. $A' \cap C = \{4, 6, 8\}$

f. $A' \cap B' = \{4, 5\}$ g. $(A \cap B)' = \{1, 2, 3, 4, 5, 6, 7, 8\}$

Subsets

When all the elements of one set, B, are contained in another set, A, then B is a subset of A, written $B \subset A$. The relationship is shown visually in the Venn diagram:

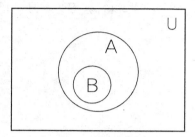

EXAMPLE 2.1.4

Let $A = \{1, 2, 3\}$ and list all the subsets of A.

SOLUTION

The subsets of A are $\{1\}$, $\{2\}$, $\{3\}$, $\{1, 2\}$, $\{1, 3\}$, $\{2, 3\}$, $\{1, 2, 3\}$, $\emptyset$. The Empty Set is a subset of every set. The set $\{1, 2, 3\}$ is considered a proper subset of A because it is a subset that is equal to the set. If a subset is a proper subset, the notation used is "$\subseteq$," so $\{1, 2, 3\} \subseteq A$.

Sets are basic building blocks of many mathematical ideas and are very useful. They are also useful as a subject in and of itself, and working with set operations is an interesting mathematical exercise.

2.1 Problem Set

1. Consider the set M = {months of the year} and list the elements for each set described.

    a. F = {months with 5 or fewer letters}

    b. Y = {months that end in "y"}

    c. S = {months with 2 syllables}

    d. E = {months with 35 days}

    e. U = {months that start with "J" and end in "y"}

    f. I = {months that start with a vowel or end in "ber"}

    g. D = {months that start with an "M" and have 1 syllable}

2. Consider the set C = {continents on Earth} and list the elements for each set described.

   a. A = {continent names that start with "A"}

   b. E = {continent names that begin and end with the same letter}

   c. T = {continent names that have 2 words}

   d. S = {continents that are islands}

3. Given the Universal set $U = \{2, 4, 6, 8, 10, 12, 14, 16, 18, 20\}$ with

   $A = \{2, 4, 6, 8, 10, 12\}$ $B = \{10, 12, 14, 16\}$ $C = \{12, 14, 16, 18, 20\}$

List the element in each of the sets:

    a. $A \cap B$ b. $A \cap C$

    c. $B \cap C$ d. $(A \cap B) \cap C$

    e. $A \cup B$ f. $A \cup C$

    g. $B \cup C$ h. $A \cup B \cup C$

    i. $(A \cup B) \cap C$ j. $(A \cap B) \cup C$

4. Give the Universal Set $U = \{1, 2, 3, 4, 5, 6, 7, 8, 9, 10\}$ with

$A = \{1, 2, 3, 4, 5, 6\}$ $B = \{4, 5, 6, 7, 8\}$

a. A' b. B'

c. $A \cap B$ d. $(A \cap B)'$

e. $A' \cap B'$ f. $A \cup B$

g. $(A \cup B)'$ h. $A' \cup B'$

5. Given the Universal Set $U = \{1, 2, 3, 4, 5, 6, 7, 8, 9, 10, 11, 12, 13, 14, 15\}$ with

$O = \{1, 3, 5, 7, 9, 11, 13, 15\}$ $E = \{2, 4, 6, 8, 10, 12, 14\}$

$M = \{5, 6, 7, 8, 9, 10\}$ $S = \{1, 2, 3, 4, 5, 6\}$

List the elements in each of the sets:

a. $O \cup M$ b. $(E \cup S) \cap M$

c. $(M \cap E) \cup S$ d. $S' \cup M$

e. $(O \cap M) \cup E$ f. $(M \cup E)'$

g. $E - M$ h. $(E \cap M)'$

i. $S' \cup E'$ j. Which two sets (O, E, M, and S) are disjoint?

2.1 Solutions

1. a. F = {March, April, May, June, July}

    b. Y = {January, February, May, July}

    c. S = {April, July, August}

    d. E = ∅

    e. U = {January, July}

    f. I = {April, August, September, October, November, December}

    g. M = {March, May}

2. a. A = {Asia, Antarctica, Australia, Africa, Europe}

    b. E = {Asia, Antarctica, Australia, Africa}

    c. T = {North America, South America}

    d. S = {Antarctica, Australia}

3. a. $A \cap B = \{10, 12\}$ b. $A \cap C = \{12\}$

    c. $B \cap C = \{12, 14, 16\}$ d. $(A \cap B) \cap C = \{12\}$

e. $A \cup B = \{2, 4, 6, 8, 10, 12, 14, 16\}$

f. $A \cup C = \{2, 4, 6, 8, 10, 12, 14, 16, 18, 20\}$

g. $B \cup C = \{10, 12, 14, 16, 18, 20\}$

h. $A \cup B \cup C = \{2, 4, 6, 8, 10, 12, 14, 16, 18, 20\}$

i. $(A \cup B) \cap C = \{12, 14, 16\}$

j. $(A \cap B) \cup C = \{10, 12, 14, 16, 18, 20\}$

4. a. $A' = \{7, 8, 9, 10\}$

b. $B' = \{1, 2, 3, 9, 10\}$

c. $A \cap B = \{4, 5, 6\}$

d. $(A \cap B)' = \{1, 2, 3, 7, 8, 9, 10\}$

e. $A' \cap B' = \{9, 10\}$

f. $A \cup B = \{1, 2, 3, 4, 5, 6, 7, 8\}$

g. $(A \cup B)' = \{9, 10\}$

h. $A' \cup B' = \{1, 2, 3, 7, 8, 9, 10\}$

5. a. $O \cup M = \{1, 3, 5, 6, 7, 8, 9, 10, 11, 13, 15\}$

b. $(E \cup S) \cap M = \{5, 6, 8, 10\}$

c. $(M \cap E) \cup S = \{1, 2, 3, 4, 5, 6, 8, 10\}$

d. $S' \cup M = \{5, 6, 7, 8, 9, 10, 11, 12, 13, 14, 15\}$

e. $(O \cap M) \cup E = \{2, 4, 5, 6, 7, 8, 9, 10, 12, 14\}$

f. $(M \cup E)' = \{1, 3, 11, 13, 15\}$

g. $E - M = \{2, 4, 12, 14\}$

h. $(E \cap M)' = \{1, 2, 3, 4, 5, 7, 9, 11, 12, 13, 14, 15\}$

i. $S' \cup E' = \{1, 3, 5, 7, 8, 9, 10, 11, 12, 13, 14, 15\}$

j. O and E are disjoint sets

Venn Diagrams

Venn diagrams were introduced in the previous section to provide a visual for representing the intersection and the union of two sets and also to show the complement of a set and subset of a set. Venn diagrams help students see relationships between sets and allow students to talk about sets without getting so involved in the mathematical language and symbolism.

As a first-grader, my daughter was presented with the following Venn diagram one morning as she entered her classroom:

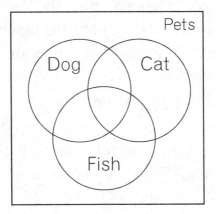

It was the first week of class, and the teacher wanted to learn more about her students and for them to learn about each other. Most students could read the word "dog," "cat," and "fish" or they asked for help from their peers, and then they were able to put their name in the appropriate spot in the Venn diagram and also explain why the spot they chose was appropriate. Here is the Venn diagram with some responses:

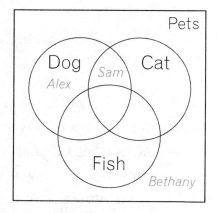

Bethany has neither a dog nor a cat nor a fish, so her name is outside all three circles. Sam has a dog and a cat but no fish, so his placement is correct. Alex has a dog but no cats or fish, and he knew just where to place his name. When talking about the Venn diagram, each child's placement, and asking about their pets, the teacher can also sprinkle the conversation with the ideas of intersection and subset as appropriate, planting those terms in their minds—early math seeds that will continue to grow and mature through the years.

As students mature mathematically, Venn diagram problems can become more challenging. Even though there are no numbers involved, the relationships between the sets can be thought of as a big abstract puzzle, and working through the problem is very mathematical.

EXAMPLE 2.2.1 Relationships with Venn diagrams

At the Sheppard Garden Store, there was a preseason sale on certain trees. Consider the following sets:

M = {Maple trees}

C = {Crabapple trees}

O = {Oak trees}

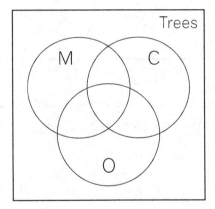

Will bought a Maple tree and a Crabapple tree but not an Oak tree. Place a W in all the region(s) that could represent Will's purchases.

Jodie bought a Crabapple tree. Place a J in all the region(s) that could represent Jodie's purchases.

Sara bought a Maple and an Oak tree. Place an S in all the region(s) that could represent Sara's purchases.

Keith bought an Oak tree but not a Crabapple tree or a Maple tree. Place a K in all the region(s) that could represent Keith's purchases.

SOLUTION

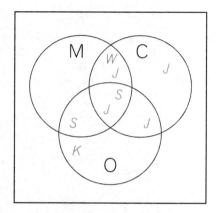

Identifying specific regions in a Venn diagram can also reinforce the ideas of intersection, union, and complement of sets.

EXAMPLE 2.2.2 Intersection, Union, and Complement with Venn diagrams

Shade the region that represents each of the following sets in the Venn diagram:

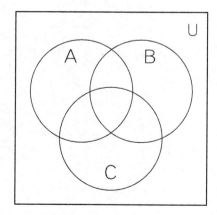

a. $A \cup B$ b. $B \cup C'$ c. $A \cup (B \cap C)$ d. $A \cap (B \cap C)'$

SOLUTION

a. In this problem, you want to find the union of the two sets, so you would shade all the regions in set A or set B, including the region they have in common.

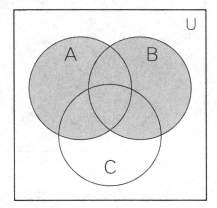

b. In this case, the complement goes first, so you would identify C', everything except set C. Then you would add in any part of set B that isn't shaded. That seems contradictory because you would include the part of B that intersects with set C. That is fine because that part is in set B. Remember with the union you have one set or the other or both.

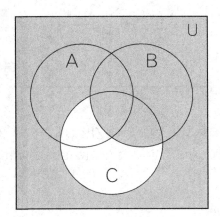

c. In this case, you would do what is in the parentheses first, so identify the intersection of sets B and C and then add in any part of set A that is not already shaded.

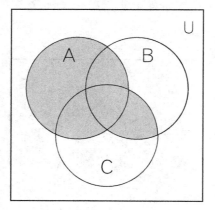

d. Here, you would first identify the intersection of set B and C and then find the complement of that set. Then, you would look to see what part of that set intersects with set A.

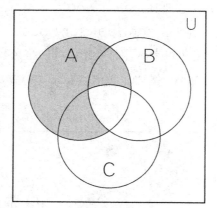

Often, numbers are added to Venn diagrams to represent how many members are in each set. This leads to some interesting problems in counting.

EXAMPLE 2.2.3 Counting sets with Venn Diagrams

Key Club members at Williston Central School are volunteering at a Special Olympics Relay event. Many members of the Key Club have signed up for the morning session or the afternoon session or for both sessions. The session attendance is given in the Venn diagram:

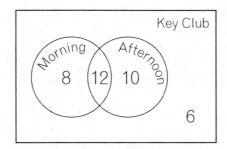

a. How many Key Club members helped out at the event?

b. How many Key Club members helped out at both the morning and afternoon sessions?

c. How many Key Club members helped out in the afternoon session?

d. How many Key Club members helped out in the morning session only?

e. How many Key Club members were unable to help in the event?

f. What is the membership of the Williston Key Club?

SOLUTION

a. 30 members

b. 12 members

c. 22 members

d. 8 members

e. 6 members

f. 36 members

Venn diagrams help reinforce the ideas of intersection, union, and complement of sets implicitly. They also introduce students to abstract thinking in an accessible, visual format. Exposing students to Venn diagrams whenever appropriate will prove beneficial as they learn new math concepts.

2.2 Problem Set

1. Mr. London is the sixth-grade track and field coach. A number of his athletes won ribbons in events at the last track meet. After the meet, he represented the ribbon winners in the following Venn diagram:

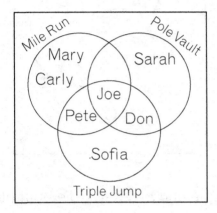

a. Whose performance was best overall?

b. Who won a ribbon in at least two events?

c. Who won a ribbon in exactly one event?

d. Who won a ribbon in the pole vault and mile run?

2. At the Pantone family reunion, there were three types of pies for dessert at the events: apple pie, blueberry pie, and cherry pie. Consider the following sets:

A = {Apple Pie}   B = {Blueberry Pie}   C = {Cherry Pie}

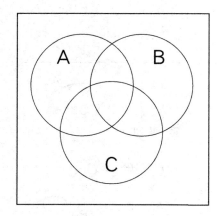

a. Jodie had apple pie and blueberry pie but not cherry pie. Place a J in the region(s) that represent Jodie.

b. Petra had blueberry pie but did not have cherry pie or apple pie. Place a P in the region(s) that represent Petra.

c. Shalaya had apple pie and cherry pie. Place an S in the region(s) that represent Shalaya.

d. Luis hates blueberries and cherries, but he did have pie. Place an L in the region(s) that represent Luis.

e. Kayla had blueberry pie and apple pie. Place a K in the region(s) that represent Kayla.

3. A group of teachers at Cooper High School attended a conference on Saturday. There was a morning session and an afternoon session, and each teacher attended at least one of the sessions. The session attendance is given below in the Venn diagram:

Morning   Afternoon

23 (8) 72

a. How many teachers attended the conference?

b. How many teachers attended both sessions?

c. How many attended the morning session?

d. How many attended only the morning session?

e. How many attended only the afternoon session?

4. A Running Club holds races each weekend. There are competitions for 100m, 200m, and 400m distance races. On a particular Saturday, the following occurred:

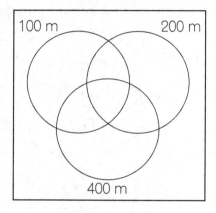

14 athletes ran the 100m

14 athletes ran the 200m

2 athletes ran the 100m, the 200m, and the 400m

5 athletes ran only the 400m

3 athletes ran the 100m and the 200m but not the 400m

8 athletes ran the 200m and the 400m

18 athletes ran the 400m

a. Fill in the Venn diagram to show the number of athletes in each
   section.

b. How many athletes ran in either the 100m, the 200m, or the 400m?

c. How many athletes ran in the 100m and the 400m?

d. How many athletes did not run in the 200m?

e. How many athletes ran in the 100m and the 400m but not the 200m?

f. How many athletes ran in the 200m or the 400m but not the 100m?

5. Shade the region that represents each of the following sets in the given Venn diagram:

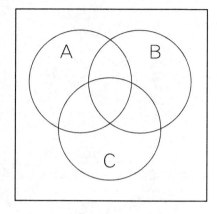

a. B ∩ C

b. B ∩ A

c. C ∩ A

d. (B ∩ C) ∩ A

e. $B \cup C$

f. $B \cup A$

g. $(B \cup C) \cup A$

h. $C' \cup (A \cap B)$

i. $B' \cap (C \cap A)$

j. $(B \cap C \cap A)'$

2.2 Solutions

1. a. Joe

   b. Pete, Don, Joe

   c. Mary, Carly, Sarah, Sofia

   d. Joe

2.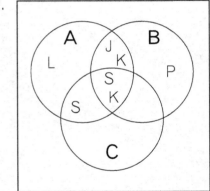

3. a. 103 teachers attended

   b. 8 attended both sessions

   c. 31 attended the morning session

   d. 23 attended only the morning session

   e. 72 attended only the afternoon session

4. a.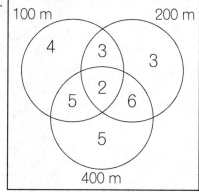

    b. 28

    c. 7

    d. 14

    e. 5

    f. 14

5. a.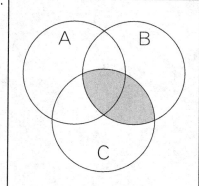

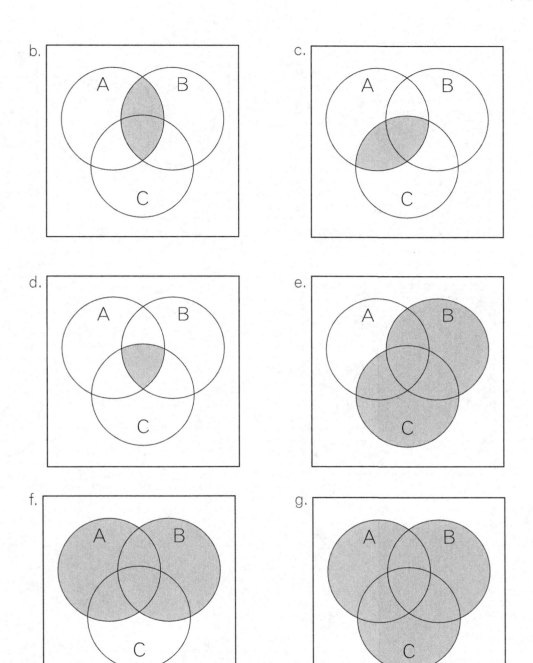

h.

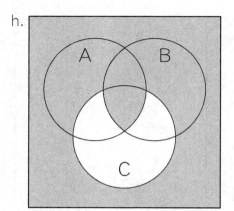

i.

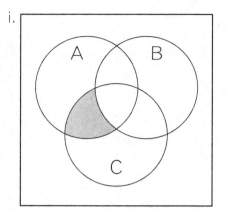

j.

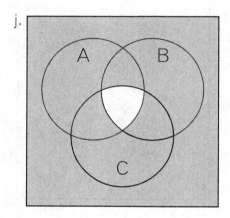

"Arithmetic is being able to count up to twenty without taking off your shoes."

—Mickey Mouse

CHAPTER 3

Whole Number Operations

This chapter introduces the meaning behind the operations of addition, subtraction, multiplication, and division.

Math Power Goals:

- Understand the meaning of addition, subtraction, multiplication, and division and how the operations are related.
- Expand your expertise in computations with whole numbers.
- Explore flexible methods that complement the traditional algorithms for operations of whole numbers.

Early Number Sense

Children learn to count by multiple exposures to a series of numbers—1, 2, 3, 4, 5, etc. Children can count steps, people, animals, flowers—really anything. The opportunity to count comes in real-life experience, games, and books. At first, the numbers are a list of memorized words: "one," "two," "three," etc. The actual counting comes into play when children assign a number to an object in a one-to-one correspondence, often pointing to an object as they count. Recognizing that the number associated with the last object "counts" the number of items is the beginning of counting as math students.

When talking about a number, there is a difference between the numeral and the amount. The numeral is the symbol that is used to represent the amount, so 4 is IV in roman numerals and IIII in tally marks. The numeral can change, but the amount is the count or cardinality associated with the set using a one-to-one correspondence.

As children grow, they continue to be exposed to situations where numbers and counting are used. They are able to count larger numbers, recognizing the pattern—twenty-one, twenty-two, twenty-three is similar to thirty-one, thirty-two, thirty-three and forty-one, forty-two, forty-three. Hundreds charts are also helpful to show students the patterns and the structure in our base 10 system.

Classifying numbers according to specific criteria sets the stage for understanding definitions in math and other areas. Numbers can be grouped as even or odd, greater than 5 or less than 5, one digit or two digits, etc. Playing games with cards in which the person with the largest card or smallest card "wins" can be fun and reinforce number relationships. A homemade set of cards that mix up different representations of amounts—using coins, tally, dominoes, as well as numbers—are helpful for students. They can draw a starting card and then decide if subsequent cards are "More," "Less," or the "Same" as the first card.

As much as possible, students should be allowed to work through the math in many different ways—numerically, visually, hands-on, and physically. Early math is fun and exciting and sets the tone for a lifetime of positive arithmetic and mathematical experiences!

Addition, Subtraction, Multiplication, and Division Models

In this section, you will explore what it means to add, subtract, multiply, and divide. Initially, the models will be presented in terms of whole numbers, but the models are appropriate regardless of the type of number used. As you consider the models, think back on your own early experiences and what worked for you and what didn't. You likely had some successes and maybe some troubles. Realize that you are looking back at these early math concepts now not as a student, but as a teacher. Your task is very different, as you revisit the basic operations with the perspective of looking beyond your own personal path. You are now looking to understand these topics with teaching your future students in mind.

When starting, it is very important to keep two things in mind. First, as much as possible, teach the operations through word problems. Giving students a context for the situation helps them form a mental picture and also helps them enter into the problem. Students may put up roadblocks from the very beginning and feel like they're stuck. Having a "real life" situation to give them something to work with may be just the nudge they need to get past the first step—starting—and actually work on the problem. The second important thing to keep in mind is to make liberal use of manipulatives, drawings, charts, and number lines. Anything that makes the math more accessible to students should be allowed.

Addition and subtraction

Addition and subtraction are connected. Addition is used when you know the parts and you want to find the whole, and subtraction is used when you know the whole and need to find a part.

Addition

Addition is where the operations really start. For addition, there is more a definition than a model. To add is to find the number of objects in the union of two disjoint sets. When adding, you combine two parts to form a whole.

Union Addition Model

"Mary brought 3 cakes for the bake sale. Jodie brought 5 cakes for the bake sale. How many cakes are there in all?"

Mary   Jodie

Subtraction

When considering subtraction, you probably think of subtraction as "take-away." The Take-Away Model is one way to think about subtraction, but there are others.

Take-Away Subtraction Model

"Serenity has 5 flowers. If she gives 2 of them to her best friend Jasmine, how many will Serenity have left?"

Comparison Model

"Tate read 6 books last week. Jordan read 3 books last week. How many more books did Tate read than Jordan last week?"

Missing Addend Model

"Bill has read 8 pages in his book. If the book has 14 pages, how many more pages does Bill have to read?"

You may have noticed that in the examples provided above, there are no equations associated with the problems that were presented. This is deliberate and is meant to help you understand the important Math Power Point listed at the beginning of the section: addition and subtraction are connected. With each of the problems above, the question to ask to get your student started is not "Should you add or subtract here?" but "Are you finding the part or the whole in this problem?" If you are finding the whole, you have an addition problem, and if you are finding a part, you have a subtraction problem. The equation you use is less important than the answer you find and making sure your answer makes sense in the context of the problem. This is also where your students will start to develop their own individual Math Power. Another important aspect of this is that by having students share the way they approached a problem, the rest of the class learns that sometimes there are many ways to get the correct answer to a math problem, and they learn from each other.

Looking at the situation given in the Missing Addend Model, this is a subtraction model because you need to find a part. But both $8 + ? = 14$ or $14 - 8 = ?$ are perfectly acceptable equations that can be used to solve this problem. The important thing is not whether students use a "+" or "-" in the equation, but that they recognize that if they are finding a part, it is subtraction, and if they are finding a whole, it is addition.

EXAMPLE 3.2.1

For each problem,

    a. State whether you are finding a part or a whole in the problem.

    b. Give a model that would be appropriate for the problem.

c. Create a number sentence for the problem.

1. Drew caught 6 fish on Saturday. If he ate 2 fish for supper, how many fish are left?

2. Warrick made 2 bowls in ceramics class during the morning session. He made 4 bowls in the afternoon session. How many bowls did Warrick make in all?

3. Erin scored 4 goals in a lacrosse game. Her friend Jessica scored 3 goals in the same game. How many more goals did Erin score in the game?

4. There are 12 pieces in Marion's puzzle. If she has correctly fit 8 pieces in the puzzle, how many pieces does she still have to place before the puzzle is completed?

SOLUTION

1. a. Part   b. Take-Away Model   c. $6 - 2 = ?$

2. a. Whole   b. Union Model   c. $2 + 4 = 6$

3. a. Part   b. Comparison Model   c. $4 - 3 = ?$ or $3 + ? = 4$

4. a. Part   b. Missing Addend   c. $12 - 8 = ?$ or $8 + ? = 12$

Solving problems is different than adding and subtracting. Adding and subtracting is a skill that you use to find the solution to a problem. Problem solving is more complex and involves more than just the answer, as mentioned earlier in this book. Having said that, it is important that students also work on their addition and subtraction facts. Knowing addition and subtraction facts well makes math easier, much the same way that knowing how to spell makes writing easier. There are a number of strategies teachers can use—flashcards, practice problems, and timed tests, among others. One scheme that might help is to have students learn the facts not as single expressions, $3 + 2 = 5$, but as a group of related number facts or "fact families", $3 + 2 = 5$, $2 + 3 = 5$, $5 - 2 = 3$, and $5 - 3 = 2$. This also continues and reinforces the relationship between the two operations.

You may have noticed in the grouping of the number facts given above that $2 + 3 = 5$ and $3 + 2 = 5$ are both given. This observation is important and should be pointed out to students. Even better, one of your students will write the number sentence for a problem as $2 + 3$ and another student as $3 + 2$, and you will have the opportunity to gently direct your students into the realization that $a + b = b + a$ for ALL whole numbers. It is a property of whole numbers called the Commutative Property, sometimes referred to as the Turn-Around Fact. There are also other properties of whole numbers under addition. Knowing them increases the Math Power for your students, and they will think they are pretty cool.

Addition properties for whole numbers

Closure Property: If $a \in W$ and $b \in W$, then $a + b \in W$

If a whole number is added to a whole number, the answer is a whole number.

Commutative Property: $a + b = b + a$

> The order in which you add doesn't make a difference in the answer.

Associative Property: $a + (b + c) = (a + b) + c$

> The groupings you use when adding don't make a difference in the answer.

Identity Property: $a + 0 = 0 + a = a$

> If you add 0 to any number, you get the same number. This is because 0 is the identity element for addition.

Inverse Property: $a + (-a) = (-a) + a = 0$

> Every number has an inverse and if you add a number and its inverse you will get the identity element, in this case 0.

Multiplication and Division

Multiplication and division are connected. When multiplying, you know the number of groups and the number in each group and you want to find the total amount. With division, you know the total and want to find either the number of groups or the number in each group.

Multiplication

Multiplication is a way to make complicated addition problems easier. Instead of adding the same number many times, as in $4 + 4 + 4 + 4 + 4$, you can simplify the process by writing 5×4 and multiplying. This leads to the basic model for multiplication, Repeat Addition. There are other models that lead to multiplication, too, some you may not have considered.

Repeat Addition Model for Multiplication
"Bert has 5 bags and each bag has 4 marbles. How many marbles does Bert have altogether?"

Array Model for Multiplication
"Darryn has 3 shelves in his room. Each shelf has 5 trophies. How many trophies does Darryn have on display?"

Area Model for Multiplication

"Jodie's garden is 8 feet long by 4 feet wide. What is the area of Jodie's garden?"

Cartesian Product Model for Multiplication

"A florist has a special on roses. You can choose a single red, pink, white, or yellow rose with either a red or pink ribbon. How many different choices are possible?"

Varying the types of multiplication problems for students is important and helps define what multiplication means. Some students will make the transition from addition to multiplication quickly and easily, and others will take smaller steps. One model may encourage a student more than others, but the hope is for students to have a facility and ease with multiplication as they progress, similar to students' vocabulary increasing as they get older and their reading and writing skills improve.

Division

The basic model for multiplication is the Repeat Addition Model, and it shouldn't surprise you to know there is a parallel model for division called the Repeat Subtraction Model.

Repeat Subtraction Model for Division

"Kerry has 15 apples. She wants to make gift bags with 3 apples in each. How many bags can Kerry make with her apples?"

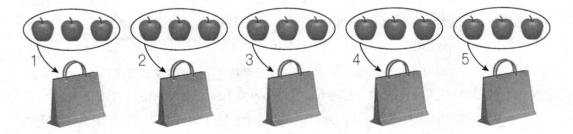

This model is used when you know the number in each group and you want to find the number of groups. The next model is when you know the number of groups and you want to find how many will be in each group.

Partition Model for Division

"Bernice has 15 flowers and 3 vases. If she wants to distribute the flowers equally among the vases, how many flowers will be in each vase?"

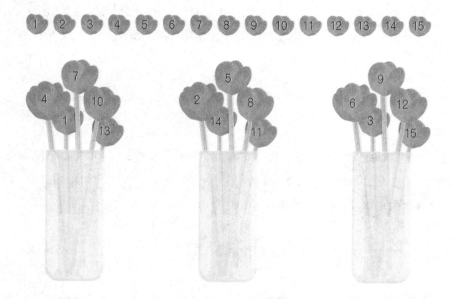

As with addition and subtraction, it is important for students to realize that there are many ways to approach a problem and many ways to find the solution. One student may divide, another may subtract, and yet another may consider multiplication for the same problem. Collaborating with other students in the class and sharing solutions, strategies, and methodology will increase the Math Power for everyone in the room, including the teacher! Even after many years teaching, I still enjoy seeing students solve math problems. And I can still be pleasantly surprised by a student coming up with a completely original, yet correct, solution to a problem. More on that in the next sections as we consider different methods of computation, but for now, some more practice with problem solving.

Example 3.2.2

For each problem,

    a. State whether you are finding the whole, the number in each group, or the number of groups in the problem.

    b. Give a model that would be appropriate for the problem.

    c. Create a number sentence for the problem.

1. Wade knits mittens and gloves and is taking orders from his friends. He has 3 colors of yarn: blue, ivory, and black. How many different possibilities are there for Wade's friends?

2. Tracey has 8 potted cacti. She wants to put 2 cacti in certain rooms in her house. How many rooms will receive the cacti?

3. Ava has hats to sell and wants to arrange them neatly on her display table. If she has 3 rows with 6 hats in each row, how many hats does Ava have to sell?

4. Ernie has 5 trays and each tray has 3 homemade chocolate truffles. How many chocolate truffles does Ernie have?

5. Milo has 12 ounces of homemade root beer that he wants to divide equally between 2 jugs. How many ounces will each jug receive?

SOLUTIONS

1. a. Find the whole   b. Cartesian   c. $2 \times 3 = ?$
   Product Model

2. a. Find the number   b. Repeat   c. $8 \div 2 = ?$ or $2 \times ? = 8$
   of groups   Subtraction
                       Model

3. a. Find the whole   b. Array Model   c. $3 \times 6 = ?$

4. a. Find the whole   b. Repeat   c. $5 \times 3 = ?$
   Model   Addition

5. a. Find the number   b. Partition   d. $12 \div 2 = ?$
   in each group   Model

Earlier in this section, the addition properties for whole numbers were listed. There are a similar set of properties for multiplication of whole numbers that I will list to complete this section.

Multiplication properties for whole numbers

Closure Property: If $a \in W$ and $b \in W$, then $a \times b \in W$

If a whole number is multiplied by a whole number, the answer is a whole number.

Commutative Property: $a \times b = b \times a$

The order in which you multiply doesn't make a difference in the answer.

Associative Property: $a \times (b \times c) = (a \times b) \times c$

The groupings you use when multiplying don't make a difference in the answer.

Identity Property: $a \times 1 = 1 \times a = a$

If you multiply any number by 1, you get the same number. This is because 1 is the identity element for multiplication.

Inverse Property: $a \times (1/a) = (1/a) \times a = 1$

Every number has a multiplicative inverse and the product of the number and its inverse is the identity element for multiplication, 1.

Zero Property: $a \times 0 = 0 \times a = 0$

If you multiply any number by 0, you get 0.

Distributive Property: $a(b + c) = ab + bc$

When multiplying a sum, you multiply all the elements in the sum.

As you continue working with math problems throughout this book, the basic models presented will come up again and again with different sets of numbers. Looking more broadly at a math problem and investigating the structure—"What type of a problem do I see here?"—is a good first step and a way to get the problem-solving process kicked into gear. Actually finding the answer to the problem is what people tend to focus on, but starting out and setting up the problem correctly is equally important.

3.2 Problem Set

For problems 1–10,

    a. State whether you are finding a part or a whole in the problem.

    b. Give a model that would be appropriate for the problem.

    c. Create a number sentence for the problem.

1. Jolene has 10 picture frames and 6 pictures. If she puts one picture in each frame, how many frames won't have a picture?

2. Maxine noticed 8 muddy footprints in the front hall. She's wiped up 5 of them. How many footprints does she have left to clean?

3. The family room has a couch and a loveseat. If there are 4 pillows on the couch and 2 on the loveseat, how many pillows are in the family room?

4. Sheila has 9 tulips that are either pink or white. If she has 5 pink tulips, how many of Sheila's tulips are white?

5. Mike brought a pizza home for supper. If his family ate 6 of the 8 pieces in the pizza, how much pizza is left for lunch tomorrow?

6. Joe has 8 kayaks available to rent each hour. If 4 of the kayaks are rented, how many are available when Jenn comes to the rent a kayak?

7. Helen has 4 math books and 5 statistics books. How many math and statistics books does Helen have altogether?

8. Jordy's shift at Chow Bella is for 8 hours. Jordy's already worked 4 hours. How many hours are left in Jordy's shift?

9. Jill bought 4 chocolates for her sister and 6 chocolates for herself. How many chocolates did Jill buy?

10. On Saturday, Tony walked 3 miles in the morning and 9 miles in the afternoon. How many miles did Tony walk on Saturday?

For problems 11–15,

    a. State whether you are finding the whole, the number in each group, or the number of groups in the problem.

    b. Give a model that would be appropriate for the problem.

    c. Create a number sentence for the problem.

11. Bree has 20 pencils and she wants to group them together in packs with 4 pencils in each pack. How many packs can she make with the 20 pencils?

12. May has 3 boxes in her bedroom. Each box has 8 stuffed animals. How many stuffed animals does May have all together?

13. Erik has 8 pounds of strawberries and 4 baskets. He wants to distribute the strawberries evenly to each basket. How may pounds of strawberries will each basket contain?

14. Anita, Pete, Doug, and Tom are all fishing together. Happily, each person caught 5 fish! How many fish did the group catch altogether?

15. Susan spent a rainy Saturday afternoon baking her delicious ChocoMonster cookies. She made a triple batch and ended up with 12 dozen cookies. Susan plans to evenly distribute her cookies to 6 families on her block. How many dozen cookies will each family receive?

For problems 16–20, determine which model best represents the given problem. Choose from the Repeated Addition Model, Area Model, Array Model, Cartesian Model, Repeat Subtraction Model, or Partition Model.

16. Janine is buying indoor/outdoor carpeting for her deck. If the deck measures 8 feet by 10 feet, how much indoor/outdoor carpeting will Janine need to buy?

17. Dan is organizing his toy cars. He has filled a case that has 8 rows and 3 columns. How many cars does Dan have in the case?

18. Georgia has 18 geraniums and 3 flower beds. If she wants to distribute her geraniums equally among each flower bed, how many geraniums will go to each flower bed?

19. Marnie makes birthday cakes for her friends. They can choose between a chocolate or white cake with maple, chocolate, mocha, or vanilla frosting. How many different possibilities are there for Marnie's cakes?

20. Helen makes cheese in 8-pound blocks, which she sells in 2-pound packages. How many packages are there in each block of cheese?

For problems 21–30, state the property represented in each statement.

21. $6 + 3 = 3 + 6$

22. $9(3 + 5) = (9 \times 3) + (9 \times 5)$

23. $5 \times (3 \times 4) = (5 \times 3) \times 4$

24. $15 \times 1 = 15$

25. $9 + 0 = 0$

26. $20 \times 4 = 4 \times 20$

27. $12 + (-12) = 0$

28. $6 \times (8 + 4) = 6 \times (4 + 8)$

29. $6 + 5$ is a real number

30. $4 \times 0 = 0$

3.2 Solutions

1. a. Part   b. Comparison or Missing Addend Model   c. $10 - 6 = ?$

2. a. Part   b. Take-Away Model   c. $8 - 5 = ?$

3. a. Whole   b. Union Model   c. $4 + 2 = ?$

4. a. Part   b. Missing Addend or Take-Away Model   c. $5 + ? = 9$ or $9 - 5 = ?$

5. a. Part   b. Take-Away Model   c. $8 - 6 = ?$

6. a. Part   b. Missing Addend or Take-Away Model   c. $4 + ? = 8$ or $8 - 4 = ?$

7. a. Whole   b. Union Model   c. $4 + 5 = ?$

8. a. Part   b. Missing Addend or Take-Away Model   c. $4 + ? = 8$ or $8 - 4 = ?$

9. a. Whole   b. Union Model   c. $6 + 4 = ?$

10. a. Whole   b. Union Model   c. $3 + 9 = ?$

11. a. Number of groups   b. Repeat Subtraction   c. $20 \div 4 = ?$

12. a. Whole   b. Repeat Addition   c. $3 \times 8 = ?$

13. a. Number in each group   b. Partition   c. $8 \div 4 = ?$

14. a. Whole   b. Repeat Addition   c. $4 \times 5 = ?$

15. a. Number in each group   b. Partition   c. $12 \div 6 = ?$

16. Area Model

17. Array Model

18. Partition Model

19. Cartesian Product Model

20. Repeat Subtraction Model

21. Commutative Property of Addition

22. Distributive Property

23. Associative Property of Multiplication

24. Identity Property for Multiplication

25. Identity Property for Addition

26. Commutative Property of Multiplication

27. Inverse Property of Addition

28. Commutative Property of Addition

29. Closure Property of Addition

30. Zero Property of Multiplication

Addition and Subtraction of Whole Numbers

In order to be a successful mathematician, you need to correctly perform the calculations needed to solve math problems. Understanding the meaning behind the operations goes hand in hand with being able to compute the solutions correctly. They are the two sides of the problem-solving coin. In this section, a number of different ways to add and subtract will be presented. You don't have to use them all. Think of them as tools that you are gathering for your math tool box. You want to be prepared for every situation that you may encounter, and the larger the tool box, the more likely you'll have the proper tool and be able to increase your Math Power!

Before we start, a couple of words about what I will call the traditional addition algorithm, the process many people use to add numbers. The traditional algorithm is very effective and the math is sound, and I'm not saying it should be ignored. I am simply going to present some alternatives and propose that these may be more effective because they allow students to calculate the answer to a math problem using techniques that make sense to them, what I like to call "inventive methods." These inventive methods vary widely and are very personal. The thread running through them all is that they throw out some commonly held ideas, such as when you add or subtract, you have to start with the ones column (guess what, you don't!), and if the number on the bottom is larger in a subtraction problem, you have to borrow (again, you don't!).

EXAMPLE 3.3.1 Traditional Addition
Solve: 34 + 57

SOLUTION

$$\begin{array}{r} 34 \\ + 57 \\ \hline 91 \end{array}$$

When adding, the steps to follow are to start with the ones column and 4 + 7 = 11, so you would "carry the 1" to the tens column and then add 1 + 3 + 5 = 9 in the tens column, so your answer is 91.

Notice that as you follow your calculations, there are some misleading statements. When adding 4 + 7 = 11, you carry the 1 over to the tens column, but why not call it "1 ten" instead of calling it a 1? Then, when adding the tens column, you have 1 + 3 + 5 = 9, but that is 1 ten + 3 tens + 5 tens = 9 tens, not just 9. Most students understand the implied place value in the traditional addition approach, but some do not. With the invented methods, the emphasis is on being true to the number and what it represents. It may take a bit to get used to since you've been adding and subtracting the same way for so long (or using a calculator to do it for you), but I assure you it will be worth the extra effort.

EXAMPLE 3.3. 2 Nontraditional Additional Methods

Solve: 34 + 57

Solution 1: $34 + 57 = 30 + 50 = 80$ (Rewriting the 3 in 34 as 30 and the 5 in 57 as 50)

$80 + 4 = 84$ (The 4 comes from the 34)

$84 + 6 = 90$ (The 6 comes from the 7 in 57)

$90 + 1 = 91$ (The 1 is the remainder from the 7 from 57)

Solution 2: $30 + 50 = 80$ (The 30 from 34 and the 50 from 57)

$4 + 7 = 11$ (The 4 in 34 and the 7 in 57)

$80 + 11 = 91$ (The sum of the two previous answers)

Solution 3: $34 + 6 = 40$ (The 6 from the 7 in 57)

$40 + 50 = 90$ (The 50 from the 57)

$90 + 1 = 91$ (The 1 is the remainder from the 7 in 57)

As you can see from the solutions above, to add using nontraditional approaches you break numbers apart and add pieces as you need them. You also write numbers in their proper form, not as a "3" in the tens column. Commonly, you look for target numbers, which combine values to create answers that are multiples of 10.

We'll now move on to subtraction, where there are even more possibilities, including not subtracting at all! Again, we'll consider the traditional algorithm and then present some nontraditional approaches.

EXAMPLE 3.3.3 Traditional Subtraction

Solve: 62 − 38

SOLUTION

```
    62
  - 38
    24
```

When subtracting here, you would first note that you can't take 8 from 2, so you would borrow a 10 from the 6 and make it a 5 and then make the 2 a 12. Then, you'd take 8 from 12, which is 4, and then take 3 from the 5 in the tens column, and that will give you 2. So the answer is 24. As you read through this explanation, notice the tens column numbers are treated as digits, not the values they represent. Most people using this algorithm understand how it works, but imagine you are working with it for the first time. It just seems very complicated! There seem to be all these rules and procedures. With the nontraditional algorithms, because the numbers are represented as their true values, there is less mystery and, hopefully, less confusion.

EXAMPLE 3.3.3 Nontraditional Subtraction—Breaking Numbers Apart

Solve: 62 − 38

SOLUTION

Solution 1:   62 − 30 = 32   (The 30 is from the 38)

32 − 2 = 30   (The 2 is from the 8 in the 38)

30 − 6 = 24   (The 6 is the remainder from the 8 in 38)

Solution 2: $62 - 32 = 30$ (The 32 is from the 38)

$30 - 6 = 24$ (The 6 is the remainder from the 38)

EXAMPLE 3.3.4 Nontraditional Subtraction—Not Borrowing

Solve: $62 - 38$

SOLUTION

$2 - 8 = -6$ and $60 - 30 = 30$
$-6 + 30 = 24$

Look at the ones column $2 - 8 = -6$. Then in the tens column, $60 - 30 = 30$. Now add the two together, and you have $-6 + 30$, which gives you 24. Skeptics will say that students don't know about negative numbers, but I think most students will be able to recognize temperatures below zero or losing yards in football and using a number line you can show them that $2 - 8 = -6$.

EXAMPLE 3.3.5 Nontraditional Subtraction—Not Subtracting

Solve: 62 − 38

SOLUTION

Now the strangest solution for a subtraction problem—not to subtract! This is simply using the Missing Addend Model for Subtraction we learned in Section 3.2.

$$38 + ? = 62$$
$$38 + 2 = 40$$
$$40 + 20 = 60$$
$$60 + 2 = 62$$

So to travel from 38 to 62, you've added $2 + 20 + 2 = 24$, so the solution to the problem is 24.

This last approach seems radical, and yet it is just as true as the others. Before the days of computerized cash registers, store clerks counted back your change in just this way. Teachers worry, saying, "What if a student doesn't learn how to subtract?" but I think that is just the point. It's not about which operation you use, it's about using an appropriate operation correctly. In this case, the Missing Addend Model of subtraction is being used, only with numbers that are larger.

Think of the possibilities—there are many. And this is where students really develop their own Math Power. They are taking these math problems and solving them in their way, using an approach that makes sense to them. How empowering! And a very positive side effect of the nontraditional methods is that students increase their accuracy because they understand the reason behind what they are doing instead of following a set of rules that make no sense to them.

Here's a final example with a problem that is often problematic because in traditional subtraction, there is a lot of borrowing, and it is hard to keep track of all of the steps.

EXAMPLE 3.3.6 Nontraditional Subtraction—Create an Easier Problem
Solve: 1000 − 286

SOLUTION

Start by taking 1 away from 1000, which gives you 999, then

999 − 286 = 713   (No borrowing necessary since you are subtracting from 9 in each column)

Now add back the 1 that you subtracted in the beginning to get the answer to the original problem:

713 + 1 = 714

Surprised by that solution? Once again, it shows the creativity that can be displayed by students when they are placed in an environment where math is more than a set of rules and number facts. Students who have a firm understanding of the operations and are allowed the freedom to explore calculations in unique ways will come up with solutions that are simple yet sophisticated. Amazing!

You don't have to start with the ones column when adding and subtracting.

Consider the number as a whole rather than each separate digit.

Reason before rules!

3.3 Problem Set

1. The Live Y-ers group has 23 students. There are 6 first-grade students, 9 second-grade students, and the remaining students are in third grade. How many students in Live Y-ers are in third grade?

2. Consider the number sentence 24 + 62 = ? + 33. What number should replace the "?" to make the number sentence true?

3. Jessie has 5 cookies. Sasha has 4 more cookies than Jessie. How many cookies do Jessie and Sasha have together?

4. Gerry is making cupcakes for the kindergarten orientation. She has 65 cupcakes. There will be 32 students in the morning orientation session and 26 in the afternoon orientation session. If each child has one cupcake, how many cupcakes will be left after the kindergarten orientation?

5. Place the digits 2, 3, 4, 5, 6, 8 in the boxes to obtain the following:

a. the largest difference

$$
\begin{array}{r}
\square\;\square\;\square \\
-\;\square\;\square\;\square \\
\hline
\square\;\square\;\square
\end{array}
$$

b. the smallest sum

$$
\begin{array}{r}
\square\;\square\;\square \\
+\;\square\;\square\;\square \\
\hline
\square\;\square\;\square
\end{array}
$$

6. Brad, Brian, and Alicia are donating books to the library's Fourth of July Book Sale. Their goal was to collect 100 books to donate. After asking friends, neighbors, and looking through their own collections, they gathered a lot of books! Brad has 26 books to donate, Brian has 47 to donate, and Alicia will donate 38. Did Brad, Brian and Alicia meet their goal of donating 100 books? How many extra books past their goal did they donate, or how many books short are they of their goal?

7. The Boy Scouts in Crystal Troop 458 sold a lot of popcorn for their yearly fundraiser. The scouts sold 41, 29, 63, 65, 17, 48, and 85 boxes of popcorn. Use compatible numbers to find the total number of boxes sold by the troop.

3.3 Solutions

1. 8 children in third grade

2. 53

3. 14 cookies

4. 7 cupcakes left over

5. $865 - 234 = 631$ for the largest difference, $246 + 358 = 604$ for the smallest sum

6. 111 books total, so over their goal of 100 by 11 books

7. 348 boxes of popcorn

Multiplication and Division with Whole Numbers

This section will be similar to the previous section, though with multiplication and division rather than addition and subtraction. Traditional methods work, but there are many other options for students. Many of the nontraditional methods are actually easier for students because they involve breaking the problem down into bite-size pieces and then combining those pieces together.

Multiplication and the Power of 10

In our number system, 10 is a very powerful number. Once students understand the meaning of multiplication, learning how to work with multiplication by 10 and powers of 10 is very helpful and serves as the basis for many nontraditional ways to perform multiplication.

Consider the product $5 \times 30 = 150$. Notice that the solution, 150, is 5×3 followed by one 0. If the problem is 50×30 the answer is 5×3 followed by two 0s or 1500. So will the answer to $5{,}000 \times 300$ be 15 followed by five 0s? Yes—$5{,}000 \times 300 = 1{,}500{,}000$. The reason this works is because our number system is a base 10 system, so multiplication by powers of 10 is very straightforward. Knowing how to multiply by powers of 10 easily is an important skill and is very useful, especially when multiplying large numbers.

EXAMPLE 3.4.1 Multiplication by Powers of 10

Solve each multiplication problem.

    a. 2×30 b. 2×300 c. $2 \times 3,000$ d. 20×30 e. 20×300 f. 200×30

SOLUTION

    a. 60   b. 600   c. 6,000   d. 600   e. 6,000   f. 6,000

Multiplication

When multiplying two larger numbers together, the traditional algorithm works but can be problematic. We'll skip over this method except to say that it emphasizes the digit (as when carrying) as opposed to thinking about the number as a whole. There is also the idea that you must start at a certain point on the right with the ones when multiplying and that when performing the multiplication, you need to multiply, then often add the digit that was carried, which can be confusing to many students. In spite of all these potential problems, many students learn the traditional algorithm and use it accurately. The goal in this section is to show some nontraditional methods that can also be presented in the classroom in the spirit of giving children alternative methods should the traditional multiplication algorithm prove difficult to master.

EXAMPLE 3.4.2 Nontraditional Approaches to Multiplication

Solve: 19×34

SOLUTION

Solution 1: Making use of the Distributive Property

19×34 $\qquad$ $10 \times 34 = 340$

$\qquad\qquad\qquad$ $9 \times 34 = 9 \times 30 = 270$

$\qquad\qquad\qquad$ $9 \times 4 = 36$

So now add together $340 + 270 + 36 = 646$

Solution 2: Use simpler numbers

$19 \times 34 = 20 \times 34 = 680$ $\quad$ (Choosing a number that is easier to work with than 19)

$680 - 34 = 680 - 30 = 650$ $\quad$ (Subtract 34 from the answer above—done in 2 steps)

$650 - 4 = 646$

Multiplication using the area model

Solve: 19×34

One of the models for multiplication presented in section 3.2 is the Area Model. Using the Area Model can be awkward with large numbers, but it can also help students see the different products that are created when multiplying. It is a visual of the method of Partial Products that follows.

Consider 19 as 1 ten and 9 ones and 34 as 3 tens and 4 ones. Create a large rectangle with the numbers along the outside as shown:

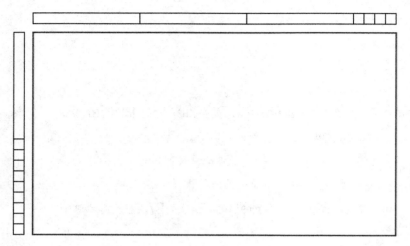

Extend the lines in the grid as shown and then identify each part, adding them together to find the product.

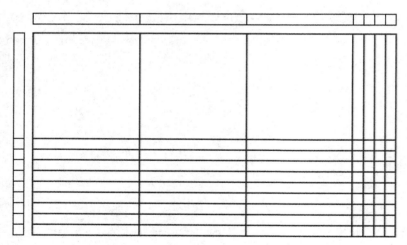

Multiplication using Partial Products

The different methods in the example show how the Distributive Property and breaking up and putting together numbers provide the reasoning behind many of the nontraditional multiplication methods. Some students will love the freedom of being able to use their own unique perspective when multiplying, and they will flourish using their inventive methods. Other students will want and need more structure when they work on problems. The method of Partial Products is a great compromise in this situation. It provides a step-by-step approach that is helpful for students who need direction, yet it still works with the number rather than the digits, so the math is truer than the traditional method.

Here's how the Method of Partial Products would work in the problem given in the previous example:

Solve: 19 × 34

$$
\begin{array}{r}
19 = 10 + 9 \\
\underline{\times\, 34 = 30 + 4} \\
36 \\
40 \\
270 \\
\underline{300} \\
646 \\
\end{array}
$$

Calculate the 4 different products, 4 × 9, 4 × 10, 30 × 9 and 30 × 10

Some people think the Method of Partial Products is too much work or too slow. This is no reason to discount a method that uses the Distributive Property and the meaning of multiplication in a way that uses numbers properly (rather than just the digit, as in "multiply by 3" when talking about the 3 in 34 instead of "multiply by 30"). If a student is struggling, he or she needs a plan and a plan that will work. One of those plans is the Method of Partial Products. And the bonus is that students get practice multiplying with powers of 10!

EXAMPLE 3.4.3 Method of Partial Products

Solve: 238 × 56

SOLUTION

$$
\begin{array}{rl}
238 = 200 + 30 + 8 & \\
\underline{\times\ 56} = 50 + 6 & \\
48 & (6 \times 8) \\
180 & (6 \times 30) \\
1200 & (6 \times 200) \\
400 & (50 \times 8) \\
1500 & (50 \times 30) \\
\underline{10000} & (50 \times 200) \\
13328 &
\end{array}
$$

Lattice Multiplication

Lattice Multiplication is another nontraditional method that students really enjoy. The beauty of this method is that the only multiplication is a one digit number times a one digit number. Also, students find all the products first and then do the addition. Lattice Multiplication has a place value system working behind the scenes in these calculations, and that is generally not obvious to the students, which makes the process seem a bit like "math magic." But if you show an example with Lattice Multiplication alongside a Partial Products problem, you can show students that both methods are the same; the organization is the only difference.

So how does Lattice Multiplication work? First, you multiply each number together and then write the answer in a box that is divided diagonally with the tens digit on the top and the ones digit on the bottom.

$3 \times 4 = 12$ and would be written this way:

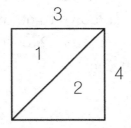

$2 \times 3 = 6$ and would be written this way, with a 0 in the tens-digit space:

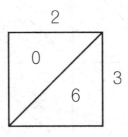

To expand this to a larger problem, here is how it would look for 19×34, the same problem worked previously using Partial Products.

19×34 would look like this:

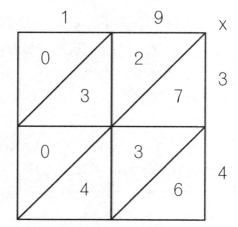

Once you've found all the products, you add along the diagonals and read the numbers from the top down to get the solution. If when adding you get an answer that is larger than 9, carry the tens digit to the next column and include it in that sum.

Here's the answer:

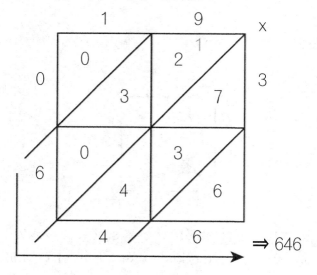

Students love Lattice Multiplication and can accurately complete large-number multiplication with the technique. Being able to do all of the multiplying first and then the addition, rather than mixing it up when using the traditional method of multiplication, is a huge advantage. In fact, even when allowed to use a calculator, some students will still use Lattice Multiplication because it is so fun to do!

EXAMPLE 3.4.4 Lattice Multiplication

Solve: 238 × 56

SOLUTION

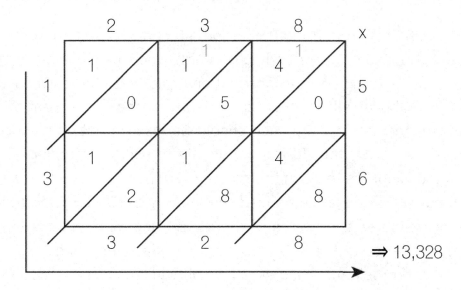

$\Rightarrow$ 13,328

Having a variety of techniques, both traditional and nontraditional, when faced with a multiplication problem gives students confidence and increases their Math Power. Some students will experiment with different methods depending on the situation, while others will rely on a few "tried and true" techniques. For many students, their "go-to" method will be Lattice Multiplication even once they are allowed to use a calculator.

Division

The traditional division algorithm is difficult for many. For some students it is the first time when they "hit the wall" mathematically, often in third or fourth grade, and they carry the fear, unease, and frustration with them from that point on. As teachers, this is definitely NOT what we want to happen, so it is even more important to give students methods to divide that make sense and are encouraging so students can get over the hump mathematically and continue their positive experience with math.

As with subtraction and multiplication, students can show great creativity and a deep understanding of math when using nontraditional methods. And some of the nontraditional methods for division don't involve dividing at all! If students understand that they want to find a quotient, the method they use should be less important than using their method accurately. To force students to use a particular method (say long division) is to cram them into a very narrow box and that may have long-lasting negative consequences. It is better to give students tools they can use and then give them the freedom to choose the one that makes sense to them. In this way, you are reinforcing their math maturity and problem-solving skills, which will lead to satisfaction and excitement when performing division and other problems in the future.

EXAMPLE 3.4.5 Nontraditional Approaches to Division

Solve: 246 ÷ 18

SOLUTION

Solution 1: Using the Partition Model

One way to think of this is to consider 18 people and 246 pieces of candy. How many will each receive?

Here is a diagram to represent this model:

People (Groups):   1 2 3 4 5 6 7 8 9 10 11 12 13 14 15 16 17 18
Give each group
10 to start: 10 10 10 10 10 10 10 10 10 10 10 10 10 10 10 10 10 10

There are 66 left: 1 1 1 1 1 1 1 1 1 1 1 1 1 1 1 1 1 1
There are 48 left: 1 1 1 1 1 1 1 1 1 1 1 1 1 1 1 1 1 1
There are 30 left: 1 1 1 1 1 1 1 1 1 1 1 1 1 1 1 1 1 1
There are 12 left

So each person (group) has 13 and there is a remainder of 12.

Solution 2: Division as Repeat Subtraction

How many 18s are there in 246? That is what division means. One way to find the answer is to see how many times you can subtract 18 from 246.

① $246 - 18 = 228$ ② $228 - 18 = 210$ ③ $210 - 18 = 192$ ④ $192 - 18 = 174$
⑤ $174 - 18 = 156$ ⑥ $156 - 18 = 138$ ⑦ $138 - 18 = 120$ ⑧ $120 - 18 = 102$
⑨ $102 - 18 = 84$ ⑩ $84 - 18 = 66$ ⑪ $66 - 18 = 48$ ⑫ $48 - 18 = 30$
⑬ $30 - 18 = 12$

Because 12 is less than 18, you can't subtract any more 18s. So your answer is 13 remainder 12.

Solution 3: Using Multiplication to solve a Division Problem

$18 \times 10 = 180$ $246 - 180 = 66$

$18 \times 3 = 54$ $66 - 54 = 12$

Putting this together, you see that $246 = 13 \times 18 + 12$, so the answer to the division problem is 13 remainder 12.

In each of the solutions, students used the definition of division-finding the number of groups or finding the number of each group-using unique ways. Some methods were straightforward, though unusual (Multiplication to Divide), and some had the potential for mistakes (Repeat Subtraction), but each method allows the student to interact with the numbers in a way that incorporates small steps and allows the student to see the calculations as they occur. These methods are very transparent.

The flaw in the nontraditional methods is that there are a lot of steps, and it would be easy for a student to make a small mistake at any point in the process. Some of the methods are cumbersome and take a while to execute. Is there a way to streamline the division process but do it in a way that the student can still stay connected to the math involved? This last method combines multiplication and the Repeat Subtraction Model, and is called Grouped Repeat Subtraction.

Grouped Repeat Subtraction

In Grouped Repeat Subtraction, you subtract large multiples of a number, usually 5 or 10, that are easy to calculate. It also allows you to use previous answers to help inform the next step. There is also a lot of flexibility in this situation. If you subtract a number that is too small, simply subtract something larger or subtract multiple times. Just make sure to keep track of how often you subtract.

Here's how it works in solving 682 ÷ 23:

First, you would think of a multiple of 23 that you could subtract from 682, often a power of 10. Since 23 × 10 = 230 and 23 × 20 = 460, either of these will work. Note that 23 × 30 = 690, so that is too much, but it does give you some information about the answer. The answer will be less than 30, a very helpful fact to know.

```
23 | 682
       230    | 10
     ─────
       452
       230    | 10
     ─────
       232
```

Now you want to know how many 23s you need to subtract from 222. You know the answer is less than 10, because if it were more than 10, the number would be higher than 230. Try doubling 23 and subtracting 46 a number of times until you have a number less than 46. Then subtract 23 until you have a number less than 23, which would be the remainder. You keep track of how many times you multiply on the side. When you get a number less than 23, in this case 15, you are done. Then add up how many times you've subtracted 23, which is 29, and note the remainder of 15.

$$
\begin{array}{r|l}
23 \,\big|\ 682 & \\
\quad\ \ 230 & 10 \\
\hline
\quad\ \ 452 & \\
\quad\ \ 230 & 10 \\
\hline
\quad\ \ 222 & \\
\quad\ \ \ \ 46 & 2 \quad \Rightarrow 29 \\
\hline
\quad\ \ 176 & \\
\quad\ \ \ \ 46 & 2 \\
\hline
\quad\ \ 130 & \\
\quad\ \ \ \ 46 & 2 \\
\hline
\quad\ \ \ \ 84 & \\
\quad\ \ \ \ 46 & 2 \\
\hline
\quad\ \ \ \ 38 & \\
\quad\ \ \ \ 23 & 1 \\
\hline
\quad\ \ \ \ 15 &
\end{array}
$$

Remainder

$$
\begin{array}{r}
29\ \text{R}\ 15 \\
23\ \big|\ 682
\end{array}
$$

Grouped Repeat Subtraction is similar to the nontraditional methods used in example 3.4.5 in methodology, but it improves on those methods in organization and structure. The benefit of this method is that students don't have to start by dividing by the largest number of times the divisor "goes into" the number. In the worked example, if you subtract 230 (23 × 10) and then realize that you can subtract again, you just subtract again. You just have to keep track on the side every time you subtract. When subtracting 23 near the end of the problem, you can subtract 23, 46 (2 × 23), or 69 (3 × 23), all easy multiples that you can do in your head. Again, all you have to do is keep track of the number of times. This method is less anxiety-producing for students because you don't have to use the correct number at every step. If you're wrong, you subtract more—you don't have to erase and agonize. It is a much more relaxed approach, and students have more success because they are less stressed when doing the calculations.

EXAMPLE 3.4.6 Grouped Repeat Subtraction

    a. Solve: 776 ÷ 35

    b. Solve: 1054 ÷ 62

    c. Solve: 2584 ÷ 53

    d. Solve: 3499 ÷ 263

SOLUTIONS

a.

$$35 \overline{\smash)776} \quad \begin{array}{r} 22 \quad R6 \\ \hline \end{array}$$

	22	R6
35	776	
	350	10
	426	
	350	10
	76	
	35	1
	41	
	35	1
	6	

b.

	17	
62	1054	
	620	10
	434	
	124	2
	310	
	124	2
	186	
	124	2
	62	
	62	1
	0	

c.

	48	R40
53	2584	
	1060	20
	1524	
	1060	20
	464	
	106	2
	358	
	106	2
	252	
	106	2
	146	
	106	2
	40	

d.

	13	R80
263	3499	
	2630	10
	869	
	263	1
	606	
	263	1
	343	
	263	1
	80	

Students should now know the meaning behind each of the operations and also have a variety of methods available to find the solutions to problems. The idea is to give students many tools to use and then, hopefully, they will find the tools that work best for them. It is similar to a carpenter who has a favorite hammer. The carpenter does beautiful work with his or her hammer, and that is a good thing. As the carpenter becomes more experienced and his or her jobs become more complex, more tools are added to the tool box. However, the favorite hammer is still there—ready when needed.

3.4 Problem Set

1. The sixth-grade class at Jefferson Middle School is raffling off a Kindle as a money-making project. If the Kindle costs $420 and the raffle tickets are sold at $5 each, how many tickets will have to be sold for the class to make a profit of $200?

2. There are 24 children in the Discovery Zone Preschool. If each child caught 6 tadpoles on a recent field trip, how many tadpoles will they be able to watch develop in the classroom aquarium?

3. There are 18 monkeys in the Rogers Valley Zoo. Each monkey has a diet that includes 15 pounds of fruit each week. How much fruit is needed to feed the monkeys each week?

4. Kerry has some landscaping she wants to work on during her summer vacation. She needs to rent a truck to help transport plants, mulch, and dirt to her house and then bring yard trash to the local composting facility. The rental agency charges $60 and then $20 per day for the truck rental. If Kerry uses the truck for 4 days, what is the rental fee for the truck?

5. Meadow Lake School gives each teacher a spring bouquet at the end of each school year. Funds are raised by the PTA. This year, there are 48 teachers at the school, and the bouquets will cost $36 each. How much will the PTA need to raise to pay for the bouquets?

6. The Eden Falls Youth Football Organization is buying footballs for the season. They need 62 standard footballs that cost $38 each and 75 youth footballs that cost $28 each. How much will the Eden Falls Youth Football Organization spend on footballs?

7. Casey sees a herd of elephants and counts 52 legs. How many elephants are in the herd?

8. The Brownsville Library is purchasing a number of paperweights to present to donors at the Friends of the Library banquet. Paperweights cost $32 each and the budget is $1,400. How many paperweights can the library purchase? How much money will be left in the budget after the purchase?

9. Mary Edna purchased 128 notebooks to distribute in backpacks for children starting school in the fall. If each backpack will receive 8 notebooks, how many backpacks can Mary Edna fill?

10. A library has 1,222 books that need to be checked for damage after a flood. The books are distributed on shelves with 26 books on each shelf. How many shelves need to be checked in order to look at every book?

11. Saraphina has 790 poker chips that need to be put in bags of 14. How many bags will Saraphina be able to fill with her poker chips?

12. Use both Lattice Multiplication and the Method of Partial Products to determine the solution to each problem.

    a. 62 × 87

    b. 245 × 39

    c. 251 × 439

13. Use the Method of Grouped Repeat Subtraction to find the solution to each problem.

    a. $812 \div 35$

    b. $7{,}070 \div 62$

    c. $9{,}188 \div 204$

3.4 Solutions

1. 124 tickets should be sold to make a profit of $200

2. 144 tadpoles

3. 270 pounds of fruit each week

4. $140 to rent the truck for 4 days

5. $1,728 for the bouquets

6. $2,356 for the standard footballs and $2,100 for the youth footballs, which totals $4,456 for all footballs

7. 13 elephants

8. 43 paperweights can be purchased with $24 left over

9. 16 backpacks

10. 47 shelves

11. 56 bags with 6 chips left over

12. a. 5394   b. 9,555   c. 110,189

13. a. 23 R 7   b. 114 R 2   c. 45 R 8

Prime Numbers and Factoring

Understanding the operations of whole numbers is critical, but there is a very important subset of the whole numbers that will be helpful as you move through the math curriculum, and that is the prime numbers.

Prime Numbers

Prime numbers are whole numbers greater than 1 with exactly two factors: 1 and itself. The number 7 is a prime number because the only factors of 7 are 7 and 1. The number 2 is the only even prime number. This is true because every other even number would have 2 as a factor. If a number is not a prime number, it is a composite number. The number 1 is neither prime nor composite; it's just 1.

EXAMPLE 3.5.1

Classify each number as prime or composite.

    a. 17

    b. 27

    c. 37

SOLUTION

    a. 17 is a prime number whose factors are 1 and 17

    b. 27 is a composite number whose factors are 1, 3, 9, and 27

    c. 37 is a prime number whose factors are 1 and 37

If you want to determine whether a number is a prime number or a composite number, you need to find its factors, or the numbers that divide into it evenly. You can find factors of a number by actually doing the division, but that takes some time. There are a number of divisibility rules that help you determine if one number is a factor of another without doing the dividing.

Divisibility Rules

Divisibility Rule for 10

A number is divisible by 10 if the ones digit for the number is a 0.

Example: 42 IS NOT divisible by 10 because its ones digit is a 2, not a 0.

Example: 230 IS divisible by 10 because its ones digit is a 0.

Divisibility Rule for 5
A number is divisible by 5 if the ones digit for the number is 0 or 5.

Example: 36 IS NOT divisible by 5 because its ones digit is a 6, not a 0 or 5.

Example: 95 IS divisible by 5 because its ones digit is a 5.

Divisibility Rule for 2

A number is divisible by 2 if the ones digit for the number is 0, 2, 4, 6, or 8.

Example: 25 IS NOT divisible by 2 because its ones digit is a 5.

Example: 48 IS divisible by 2 because its ones digit is an 8.

Divisibility Rule for 4

A number is divisible by 4 if the tens and ones digits, taken as a number, are divisible by 4.

Example: 364 IS divisible by 4 because 64 is divisible by 4.

Example: 214 IS NOT divisible by 4 because 14 is not divisible by 4.

Example: 1,780 IS divisible by 4 because 80 is divisible by 4.

Divisibility Rule for 8

A number is divisible by 8 if the hundreds, tens, and ones digits, taken as a number, are divisible by 8.

Example: 3,168 IS divisible by 8 because 168 is divisible by 8.

Example: 5,188 IS NOT divisible by 8 because 188 is not divisible by 8.

Most of the divisibility rules listed above have a similar flavor. The divisibility rules for 3 and 9 are a bit different.

Divisibility Rule for 9

A number is divisible by 9 if the sum of the digits in the number is divisible by 9.

Example: 4,518 IS divisible by 9 because $4 + 5 + 1 + 8 = 18$ and 18 is divisible by 9.

Example: 2,215 IS NOT divisible by 9 because $2 + 2 + 1 + 5 = 10$ and 10 is not divisible by 9.

Divisibility Rule for 3

A number is divisible by 3 if the sum of the digits in the number is divisible by 3.

Example: 357 IS divisible by 3 because 3 + 5 + 7 = 15 and 15 is divisible by 3.

Example: 263 IS NOT divisible by 3 because 2 + 3 + 6 = 11 and 11 is not divisible by 3.

Example: 5,787 IS divisible by 3 because 5 + 7 + 8 + 7 = 27 and 27 is divisible by 3. (A bonus here is that you also know that 5,787 is divisible by 9 because 27 is also divisible by 9!)

Now let's get back to determining if a number is prime number or a composite number. Consider the number 51; is it a prime number, or is it a composite number? The number 51 is not divisible by 2, 4, 8, 5, or 10. You can tell because the ones digit in 51 is a 1. You may think that 51 is prime, but you still have a few other numbers to try. The sum of the digits in 51, 5 + 1 = 6, so 51 is divisible by 3. The number 51 has a factor other than 1 and itself, so it is a composite number. Let's take that idea a bit further and find all the factors of 51. The number 51 is divisible by 1, 3, 17, and 51, so those are its factors.

Looking at the different factors of a number leads to a concern or question. What is the best way to write a number as a product of its factors? For example, should 51 be written as 1 × 51 or 3 × 17, or 1 × 3 × 17? And what about the number 12? Should 12 be written as 1 × 12, 2 × 6, 3 × 4, or 2 × 2 × 3? It seems there are a lot of different ways to write numbers in terms of their factors. Mathematicians have determined that writing a number using its prime factors is the best way to resolve the issue of multiple factorizations of a number. This is the idea in the Fundamental Theorem of Arithmetic, which states that a number greater than 1 is either a prime number or can be written uniquely (differing only by the order of the factors) as a product of prime numbers. According to the Fundamental Theorem of Arithmetic, the number 18 would be written as $18 = 2 \times 3 \times 3$ and the number 11 is prime.

Factoring Methods

If the number is small, you can often factor it in your head. For larger numbers, it's helpful to have a method that you can use to find the different factors of a number.

Factor trees

One popular method is to use a factor tree. In this method, you divide the number into two factors, then take each factor and divide that number into smaller factors. Prime factors are circled as you go. Here is a factor tree for the number 420.

$$420 = 2 \cdot 2 \cdot 3 \cdot 5 \cdot 7$$

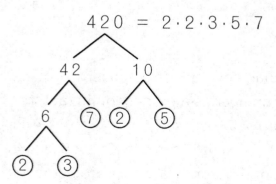

Factor trees are great, but they can be overwhelming for some students. The first step, dividing a number into two factors, can be intimidating and can lead to students becoming "stuck" and giving up on the problem. Another problem with factor trees is that students may think a number is prime and not factor it completely. This could happen with 57, which some students will think is prime rather than noticing that $5 + 7 = 12$, so 57 is divisible by 3 and is 3×19.

Smallest Prime

One other factoring method is to divide only by prime numbers, starting with the lowest prime, 2, until 2 does not divide into the number anymore, then the next-lowest prime, 3, until 3 does not divide into the number anymore, etc. You keep going until the answer is a prime. Students think this method takes longer, but it really doesn't. The advantage of this method is that students are dividing by smaller numbers, so they make fewer mistakes. Also, you keep dividing until the final answer is a prime, so you are less likely to stop prematurely. Finally, it gives students a method to use and a way to start the problem, which should lessen the number of students who get "stuck."

Here is how the method works with 420.

$$
\begin{array}{r|l}
2 & 420 \\ \hline
2 & 210 \\ \hline
3 & 105 \\ \hline
5 & 35 \\ \hline
 & 7
\end{array}
$$

To only teach factor trees is to do a disservice to your students. Even students who prefer using factor trees will appreciate having another method to check their work. Give students more factoring power by presenting two methods and letting them choose the method that works the best for them!

EXAMPLE 3.5.2

Write the prime factorization of each number.

    a. 630   b. 79   c. 325   d. 1,980   e. 8,712

    a. $630 = 2 \times 3 \times 3 \times 5 \times 7$

    b. 79 is prime

    c. $325 = 5 \times 5 \times 13$

    d. $1980 = 2 \times 2 \times 3 \times 3 \times 5 \times 11$

    e. $8,712 = 2 \times 2 \times 2 \times 3 \times 3 \times 11 \times 11$

Greatest Common Factor (GCF) and Least Common Multiple (LCM)

When working with two numbers, it is often helpful to know the Greatest Common Factor or the Least Common Multiple of the two numbers. This skill is especially helpful when reducing fractions (divide the numerator and denominator by the greatest common factor) or finding a common denominator (the least common multiple). This idea also connects with the intersection and union of two (or more) sets, as you will see when working through the problems.

Consider the two numbers 70 and 42. What are the Greatest Common Factor and Least Common Multiple of the two numbers?

In order to find the Greatest Common Factor of the two numbers, you do just what it says: you list all the factors of each number, find any factors in common, and then select the one that is the largest.

The number 70 is 1×70, 2×35, 5×14, 7×10. The factors of 70 are 1, 2, 5, 7, 10, 14, 35, and 70.

The number 42 is 1×42, 2×21, 3×14, 6×7. The factors of 42 are 1, 2, 3, 6, 7, 14, 21, and 42.

The common factors of 42 and 70 (the intersection of the two lists) are 1, 2, 7, and 14. The Greatest Common Factor between 70 and 42 is 14. This can be written as GCF(42, 70) = 14.

In order to find the Least Common Multiple of 70 and 42, you again do just what it says to do. List multiples of each number and then find the smallest multiple in both lists.

Multiples of 70 are 70, 140, 210, 280, 350, 420, 490, . . .
Multiples of 42 are 42, 84, 126, 168, 210, 252, 294, 336, 378, 420, . . .

Common Multiples (the intersection of the two lists) are 210, 420, and others. We want the smallest number in the list, which would be 210. The

Least Common Multiple between 70 and 42 is 210. This can be written as LCM(42, 70) = 210.

EXAMPLE 3.5.3

Find the Greatest Common Factor and Least Common Multiple for each set of numbers.

a. 24 and 40   b. 16 and 18 c. 15 and 4   d. 12, 10, and 30

a. GCF(24, 40) = 8 and LCM(24, 40) = 120

b. GCF(16, 18) = 2 and LCM(16, 18) = 144

c. GCF(15, 4) = 1 and LCM(15, 4) = 60

Note: 15 and 4 are examples of numbers that are relatively prime. If two numbers are relatively prime, the only factor they have in common is 1. Because of this property, the GCF of two relatively prime numbers is 1, and the LCM of two relatively prime numbers is the product of the two numbers.

d. GCF(12, 10, 30) = 2 and LCM(12, 10, 30) = 60

For the problems above, the numbers are smaller, and it is relatively easy to find the GCF by writing out the factors of each number in a list. It is also not too difficult to find the first few multiples of each number to determine the LCM. As numbers get larger, a method that incorporates prime factorization makes finding the GCF and LCM easier. This method also provides a little review of the intersection and union of two sets, an added bonus.

EXAMPLE 3.5.3 GCF and LCM with Prime Factoring

Find the Greatest Common Factor and Least Common Multiple for 252 and 270.

SOLUTION

You could solve this problem using the methods from the previous examples, but it would be a lengthy process because the numbers involved are much bigger. By prime factoring each number, we're able to see "inside" each number and use that information to stream-line the process of finding the Greatest Common Factor and Least Common Multiple.

The first step is to prime factor each number:

$252 = 2 \times 2 \times 3 \times 3 \times 7$

$270 = 2 \times 3 \times 3 \times 3 \times 5$

To find the Greatest Common Factor, you find the intersection of the two lists of prime factors. There is a factor of 2 in each number and two factors of 3 in each number. There is a 7 in one number and not the other, and it is the same with the 5. So the GCF would be $2 \times 3 \times 3 = 18$.

Next is the Least Common Multiple, and in this case, you find the union of the two lists of prime factors. The easiest way to do this is to start with one of the numbers and add in any of the other factors that haven't been listed. The LCM would be $2 \times 2 \times 3 \times 3 \times 7$ (for the 252) and add in another factor of 3 and a factor of 5 (from the 270). So the LCM will be $2 \times 2 \times 3 \times 3 \times 3 \times 5 \times 7 = 3,780$.

What happens when you multiply the GCF(252, 270) × LCM(252, 270)? That would be $18 \times 3,780 = 68,040$. And how about if you multiply 252 × 270? That is also 68,040! This is a helpful piece of information you can use to check your work when determining the GCF and LCM of two numbers. If a and b are any two whole numbers, GCF(a, b) × LCM(a, b) = a × b.

EXAMPLE 3.5.6

Find the Greatest Common Factor and Least Common Multiple for each set of numbers.

a. 1,575 and 720   b. 3,822 and 910   c. 180, 630, and 315

SOLUTION

a. GCF(1,575, 720) = 45   LCM(1,575, 720) = 25,200

b. GCF(3,822, 910) = 182   LCM(3,822, 910) = 19,110

c. GCF(180, 630, 315) = 45   LCM(180, 630, 315) = 1,260

When you determine the Greatest Common Factor and Least Common Multiple of two numbers, you are able to appreciate the relationship between the two numbers and how they interact with each other. It's as if you put both numbers under a microscope and see them on a cellular level, which is pretty cool. Giving your students opportunities to discover neat number-theory properties can provide wonder and excitement about mathematics. An added benefit with the GCF and LCM is that both come in handy when working with fractions, so they are practical as well as interesting.

3.5 Problem Set

1. Prime factor each number.

    a. 315

    b. 555

    c. 600

d. 2,730

e. 5,940

f. 8,400

2. Find the Greatest Common Factor for each pair or trio of numbers.

    a. 15 and 25

    b. 48 and 60

    c. 54 and 180

    d. 240 and 288

e. 30, 42, and 54

f. 56, 80, and 120

g. 75, 150, and 200

3. Find the Least Common Multiple for each pair or trio of numbers.

    a. 12 and 15

    b. 8 and 14

    c. 12 and 24

    d. 8 and 15

e. 16 and 28

f. 12, 18, and 15

g. 8, 12, and 20

4. Three taxi cabs make a complete trip from downtown to the airport and back in 21, 30, and 35 minutes, respectively. If all three cabs leave at the same time, what is the shortest time that must pass before they are all together again?

5. Pete's Pastry Shop is celebrating its one-year anniversary by giving away a free cookie to every 8th person who comes to the store, a free brownie to every 12th person who comes to the store, and a free pie to every 30th person who comes to the store. What person will be the first to receive a free cookie, brownie, and pie?

6. By selling cookies at 24 cents each, Jerry made enough money to buy several cans of soda costing 45 cents per can. If he had no money left over after buying the soda, what is the least number of cookies he could have sold?

7. Determine all values for the digit d that make the number 4,3d1 divisible by 3.

8. Determine all values for the digit d that make the number 53d divisible by 4.

9. Determine all values for the digit d that make the number 31,5d9 divisible by 9.

10. Determine all values for the digit d that make the number 4,23d divisible by 6.

11. Determine all values for the digit d that make the number 7,d24 divisible by 3 but not by 9.

12. Determine all values for the digit d that make the number 2,34d divisible by 15.

3.5 Solutions

1. a. $3 \times 3 \times 5 \times 7$ b. $3 \times 5 \times 37$ c. $2 \times 2 \times 2 \times 3 \times 5 \times 5$

    d. $2 \times 3 \times 5 \times 7 \times 13$ e. $2 \times 2 \times 3 \times 3 \times 3 \times 5 \times 11$ f. $2 \times 2 \times 2 \times 2 \times 3 \times 5 \times 5 \times 7$

2. a. 5   b. 12   c. 18   d. 48   e. 6   f. 8   g. 25

3. a. 60   b. 56   c. 24   d. 120   e. 112   f. 180   g. 120

4. 210 minutes

5. 120th person to come to the store

6. 15 cookies

7. 1, 4, and 7

8. 2 and 6

9. 0 and 9

10. 0 and 6

11. 2 and 8

12. 0

Image Credits

Section 3.2

"The happiness of life is made up of minute fractions—the little, soon forgotten charities of a kiss or a smile, a kind look or heartfelt compliment."

—Samuel Taylor Coleridge

CHAPTER 4

Fractions and Decimals

In this chapter, you will explore fractions and develop strategies to work with fractions to solve problems.

Math Power Goals:

- Become familiar with the structure and meaning of fractions and decimals.
- Gain understanding and skill in all fraction and decimal operations.
- Observe similarities between whole number, fraction, and decimal operations.

Fraction Concepts

More than many other math ideas, fractions seem to cause problems for math students. In this section, we'll talk about basic fraction ideas and explore different fraction models.

Fractions are everywhere. When cooking, you may have to double a recipe that calls for ¾ of a cup of flour. If you're sewing, you may have to buy 2 ¼ yards of material to create a costume. If you need to build a picture frame, you may have to cut a length of wood into 8 ½-inch pieces. In distance running, you may run a mile in 1/5 of an hour. Many daily activities involve fractions, and it's important to understand what fractions mean in order to be able to work with them.

Mathematically, fractions are rational numbers. A rational number is any number that you can write as $\frac{a}{b}$, with a an integer and b a nonzero integer. When b is 1, we have the integers, and when b is any other nonzero value, we have a fraction. A fraction is simply a part of a whole, generally thought of as 1. Fractions are written in the form $\frac{a}{b}$. The top number (or numerator), a, counts how many parts of the whole are represented. The bottom number (or denominator), b, tells the number of parts the whole is divided into. For example, in the fraction $\frac{5}{8}$ the "8" on the bottom tells you that the whole is divided into 8 equal parts. The "5" on the top tells you that you have 5 of these parts, each $\frac{1}{8}$ of the whole.

When trying to visualize fractions, many people think of a circle divided into equal pieces with some of those pieces shaded in to represent the fraction. The circle model works well in many cases, but there are other ways to represent fractions. Using different models for fraction problems provides flexibility and deepens your understanding.

Fraction Models

Region or area model

With this model, you use a geometric shape to represent the whole, and it is divided into equal parts to show the factions that make up the whole. Usually a circle, mentioned above, or a square is used to represent the whole because both shapes are easily divided into many different-sized fractional parts. Using a variety of polygons and other shapes as the whole creates a more interesting fraction representation and requires a student to think more carefully about the fraction problem.

For example, use a hexagon instead of a circle to represent a whole divided into sixths.

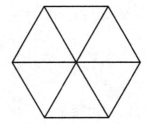

In this hexagon, the whole is divided into 6 equal pieces. Each region

represents $\frac{1}{6}$.

Here is another way to show a hexagon divided into sixths.

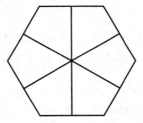

Length or Strips Model

This model is especially helpful when measuring length and comparing fractional amounts.

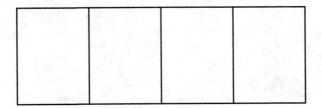

In this example, the strip is divided into 4 equal parts, so each region represents $\frac{1}{4}$.

A ruler can be used to represent a fraction using the length or strip model.

Set Model

This model is especially helpful when considering a discrete number of objects, such as a box of 8 chocolates or a bag of 12 apples, as a whole.

There are 8 balloons in the display. Each balloon would represent $\frac{1}{8}$ of the display.

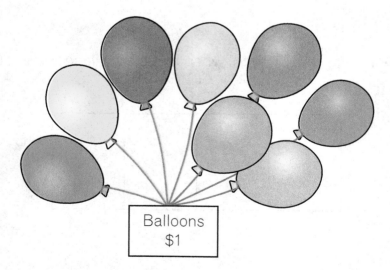

There are a few important requirements to consider when talking about fractions. First, the whole must be made up of the correct number of parts or shares. When considering a bag of 6 marbles and dividing the bag into thirds, each third would have 2 marbles. Second, each part must be equal, the same size, though it doesn't have to be congruent (the same size and shape). As you can see below, the square is divided correctly into fourths, though each piece doesn't look the same. On the other hand, the circle is not divided correctly into fourths because each region does not represent the same amount of space.

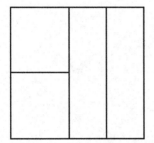 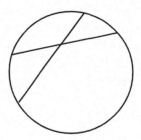

Another helpful idea to consider when talking about fractions is to remember that the more shares you have, the smaller the fractional part. This means $\frac{1}{2}$ is larger (or more) than $\frac{1}{3}$. This might be intuitively hard for young children to understand because they know that 3 is larger than 2. You might say that those relationships are reversed with fractions, but a better way might be to appeal to their stomachs. Tell them to think about sharing a pizza with one person (where each person would eat ½ of the pizza) or with two people (with each person eating 1/3 of the pizza). "In which case would you get a larger amount of food?" Most children will realize that if they share the pizza with one person rather than two, they will get more pizza to eat!

Representing Fractions

Identifying fractions is the beginning for students and an important first step.

For each of the following examples, indicate the fraction that is represented in the shaded and unshaded region.

EXAMPLE 4.1.1 Area Model

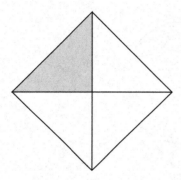

The shaded region is ¼, and the unshaded region is ¾.

EXAMPLE 4.1.2 Strip Model

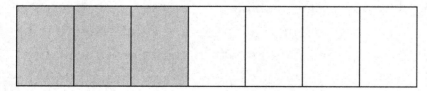

The shaded region is 3/7, and the unshaded region is 4/7.

EXAMPLE 4.1.3 Discrete Model

The fraction of the set that is shaded is 2/3, and the fraction of the set that is unshaded is 1/3.

When working with a whole, as in the above examples, you need to find how many parts the whole is divided into for the denominator and then identify the number shaded or unshaded for the numerator. Note also that the two parts, shaded and unshaded, equal the whole, as in 3 parts shaded and 4 parts unshaded would mean 7 parts altogether, and $\frac{7}{7}=1$, or the whole. This is a natural way for students to see that with a whole divided into "a" number of parts, and you have "a" of them, that represents the whole.

An interesting, open-ended problem is to give students a set as a whole and have them create the number sentence to represent the scenario. Here are some examples of how this idea could work with a set of 6 stars.

This could be represented by $\frac{3}{6}+\frac{3}{6}=1$ or $\frac{1}{2}+\frac{1}{2}=1$, depending on how the student looked at the problem. This is also a very natural way to talk about equivalent fractions.

This could be represented by $\frac{2}{6}+\frac{2}{6}+\frac{2}{6}=1$ or $\frac{1}{3}+\frac{1}{3}+\frac{1}{3}=1$.

Having open-ended questions can help you see how your students are thinking about fractions and also reinforce ideas such as $\frac{6}{6}=1$. Plus, in this type of problem, there are a variety of solutions, and students can gain extra insight looking at the work of their peers. Some students may also add designs or faces to their stars. You can change the stars to ice cream scoops in a bowl or fish in a pond to make the lesson more personal to your particular class.

Another activity is one where students use fractions to find a secret message. A simple version is listed below:

Take the first $\frac{1}{3}$ of MET   M

Take the last $\frac{1}{2}$ of WHAT   AT

Take the first $\frac{1}{5}$ of HELLO   H

Take the first $\frac{1}{3}$ of POTATO   PO

Take the last $\frac{3}{4}$ of EWER   WER

The secret message: MATH POWER

The message can easily be modified to be more or less difficult, especially in a classroom with many different ability levels. Sometimes it's nice to have the same activity for the whole class but at varied levels so all the groups can succeed.

In order to have students see the role of each part of the fraction, the top and the bottom, consider the following problem.

If "0 0 0 0 0 0 0 0 0 0 0 0" = 1, how many 0's would represent 2/3?

In order to find the answer to this problem, one would first consider that the whole has twelve 0's. To represent 2/3, you would first need to find how many 0's there are in 1/3, so you would divide 12 by 3 and realize that four 0's would be 1/3. In order to have 2/3, you would need two 1/3 parts, so that would be eight 0's for 2/3.

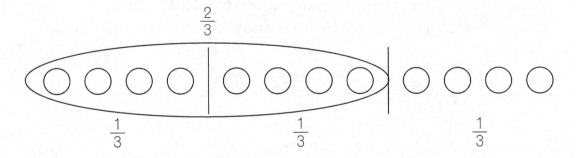

What will happen if the problem is reversed? Whenever possible, I like to have students work a problem in a different direction. This generally helps them gain a higher level of understanding and also allows you to see if they really know the meaning of what they're doing or simply memorizing a series of steps.

If "0 0 0 0 0 0 0 0 0 0 0 0" = 2/3, how many 0's would equal 1?

To solve this problem, also with twelve 0's, you can't divide by 3 because you don't have the whole. In this case, you would divide by 2; then in each part, six 0's would be 1/3. Once you have a representation for 1/3, you know 3/3 would be 1 or the whole, so you would take the six 0's and multiply by 3 to get eighteen 0's for 1.

$$\underbrace{\bigcirc\bigcirc\bigcirc\bigcirc\bigcirc\bigcirc}_{\dfrac{1}{3}}\Big|\underbrace{\bigcirc\bigcirc\bigcirc\bigcirc\bigcirc\bigcirc}_{\dfrac{1}{3}}\Big|\bigcirc\bigcirc\bigcirc\bigcirc\bigcirc\bigcirc = 1$$

Notice that when you are given a whole and asked to find a part, you divide by the bottom number (the denominator) to find out how many in each fractional part and then multiply by the number of parts you need (the numerator). But when given a part and asked to find the whole, you divide by the top number (the numerator) in order to find how many in each part and then multiply by the number of parts you need to make the whole.

EXAMPLE 4.1.4

If "# # # # # # # # # # # # # # # # # #" = 1, find 2/3.

Solution: "# # # # # #" = 1/3, so "# # # # # # | # # # # # #" = 2/3.

EXAMPLE 4.1.5

If "# # # # # # # # # # # # # # # # # #" = 2/3, find 1.

Solution: "# # # # # # # # #" = 1/3, so "# # # # # # # # # | # # # # # # # # # | # # # # # # # # #" = 3/3 = 1

EXAMPLE 4.1.6

Now that you've got that down, let's add a bit of a challenge.

If "O O O O O O O O O O O O" = 2/3, find 5/6.

This problem is great because it takes the ideas presented above to a deeper level by having the change in denominators. It's also wonderful because there are so many ways to solve this problem. Having students share their different solutions helps every student gain Math Power.

SOLUTION 1

One way to solve this problem, and a good overall strategy, is to always find the whole and work from there. Recall from the previous problem that if twelve 0's is 2/3, then eighteen 0's is 1. So now the problem becomes finding 5/6 when you know 1 is eighteen 0's. Since you know the whole, divide by 6 to find out how many 0's are in 1/6, which gives you three 0's in 1/6, then fifteen 0's in 5/6.

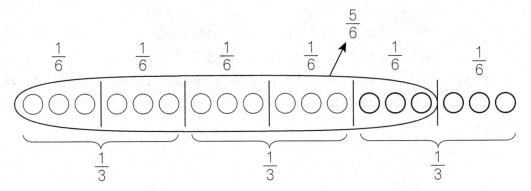

SOLUTION 2

Since twelve 0's are 2/3, dividing by 2 gives you six 0's for 1/3. From this, you can surmise that if you take half of 1/3, you would have 1/6, so 1/6 would be half as many 0's, or three 0's = 1/6. Then to get 5/6, you would multiply by 5 and have fifteen 0's for 5/6. As you can see, this is the same solution as the one given above, which is encouraging.

SOLUTION 3

Consider that 5/6 = 2.5/3, so in order to have 5/6, you would need two 1/3s and then half of a 1/3. Remember six 0's is 1/3, so 2/3 is twelve 0's. We still need another half of a third, which would be half of 6 or three 0's. Adding all the parts up, we have 12 + 3 0's, which is fifteen 0's = 5/6.

$$\bigcirc\bigcirc\bigcirc\bigcirc\bigcirc\bigcirc \big| \bigcirc\bigcirc\bigcirc\bigcirc\bigcirc = \frac{2}{3}$$

$$\frac{1}{3} \qquad\qquad \frac{1}{3}$$

$$\frac{5}{6} = \frac{2.5}{3} = \begin{array}{l} \bigcirc\bigcirc\bigcirc\bigcirc\bigcirc\bigcirc \quad \frac{1}{3} \\ \bigcirc\bigcirc\bigcirc\bigcirc\bigcirc\bigcirc \quad \frac{1}{3} \\ \bigcirc\bigcirc\bigcirc \qquad\quad \frac{.5}{3} \end{array} \Bigg\} = \frac{2.5}{3}$$

There are more problems of this type in the Exercise Set so you can work on other examples.

Manipulatives are really helpful when working with fractions. There are many available, including Cuisenaire Rods, which are a very flexible learning tool. Pattern blocks—the yellow hexagon, red trapezoid, blue rhombus, and green triangle—can also be used to great benefit. Students can bring in examples of fraction problems they see in magazines or in their day-to-day interactions.

A variety of different experiences is essential for students to have a good understanding of fractions and for them to have confidence when dealing with different types of problems. If students only see circles when working with fractions, they will think all fractions involve pies or pizzas. If they are always given the whole, then they will miss out on seeing different aspects of fractions. Throw a wide net with all different types of fraction problems for your students. They'll be more likely to be caught up in the fraction experience and find their own fraction sense and fraction power!

4.1 Problem Set

1. If XXXXXX = 1, how many X's will equal 7/12?
   XXXXXX

2. If XXXXXX = 1, how many X's will equal 2/3?
   XXXXXX

3. If XXXXXX = 1, how many X's will equal 5/6?
   XXXXXX

4. If   XXXXXXXX = 1, how many X's will equal 5/18?
        XXXXXXXX

5. If   XXXXXXXX = 1, how many X's will equal 2/3?
        XXXXXXXX

6. If   XXXXXXXX = 1, how many X's will equal 5/6?
        XXXXXXXX

7. If   XXXXXX = 2/3, how many X's will equal 1?
        XXXXXX

8. If $\dfrac{XXXXXX}{XXXXX} = 3/4$, how many X's will equal 1?

9. If $\dfrac{XXXXXX}{XXXXXX} = 3/7$, how many X's will equal 1?

10. If $\dfrac{XXXXXX}{XXXXX} = 2/3$, how many X's will equal 1/9?

11. If $\dfrac{XXXXXX}{XXXXXX} = 3/4$, how many X's will equal 5/8?

12. If   XXXXXX = 3/7, how many X's will equal 1/4?
         XXXXXX

13. If   XXXXXXXXX = 2/3, how many X's will equal 4/9?
         XXXXXXXXX

14. If   XXXXXXXXX = 3/4, how many X's will equal 2/3?
         XXXXXXXXX

15. If   XXXXXXXXX = 2/5, how many X's will equal 4/9?
         XXXXXXXXX

16. What travels around the world but stays in one spot? Solve the clues to find the answer to this riddle:

First 1/3 of street   Last ½ of clam   Middle 1/3 of ape

A   _____   _____   _____

4.1 Solutions

1. 7 X's

2. 8 X's

3. 10 X's

4. 5 X's

5. 12 X's

6. 15 X's

7. 18 X's

8. 16 X's

9. 28 X's

10. 2 X's

11. 10 X's

12. 7 X's

13. 12 X's

14. 16 X's

15. 20 X's

16. A stamp

Computations with Fractions: Addition and Subtraction

As you've progressed through this book, you've increased your Math Power and become more comfortable with operations on whole numbers. As your Math Power grows, you're able to be more informed and competent when solving problems, which leads to more success and more confidence. The same will be true as you work with fractions. The most important thing when working with fractions is to have an understanding of how fractions and fraction computation works, rather than memorizing procedures. Increasing your fraction power gives you freedom to work with fractions in a way that makes sense to you. You've already started in the first section as you explored the meaning of fractions. The next step is to see how to solve problems involving addition and subtraction of fractions.

When working with fractions, remember "REASON before RULES." The best way to ensure that students don't remember a process is to list the steps in the process without explaining the reasoning behind the steps. In this section, the plan is to build upon the addition and subtraction models used with whole numbers and couple them with the meaning behind the numerator (top number) and denominator (bottom number) in a fraction.

The following examples illustrate how fractions are added together and subtracted from each other.

EXAMPLE 4.2.1 Addition with the same Denominators

Jodie and Pete are having pizza for dinner. The pizza is divided into 8 slices. If Jodie ate 1/8 of the pizza and Pete ate 2/8 of the pizza, what fraction of the pizza did they eat together?

First, you may want to draw a picture and illustrate the scenario. A typical drawing is shown below:

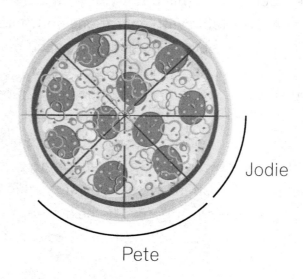

Jodie

Pete

Next, consider that the problem asks to find the amount eaten altogether by Jodie and Pete. This leads us to think that this is an addition problem.

The amount eaten by Jodie is 1/8 and the amount eaten by Pete is 2/8. The amount they eat together is represented by 1/8 + 2/8. What is the answer?

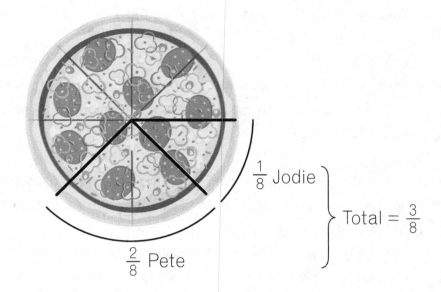

As you can see by the diagram, the total amount eaten by Jodie and Pete is 3/8. So 1/8 + 2/8 = 3/8.

Notice that when computing the solution, the numerators are added, but the denominators are not—they remain the same. This makes sense when you recall the roles played by the numerator and the denominator of a fraction. The numerator tells you "how many," and the answer in this problem is 1 + 2, or 3. The denominator tells you the number of parts, and that is still eighths. So you end up with 3/8 for the answer for the amount eaten by Jodie and Pete—3 parts, and those parts happen to be eighths in this problem.

The answer would be similar if the problem had been "Jodie ate 1 cookie and Pete ate 2 cookies. How many cookies did they eat together?" In this case, the problem would be represented by 1 + 2 = 3 and the 3 would be cookies. The answer is the same, but the label has changed. Instead of having cookies, you're having eighths, but you still have 3 of something eaten by Jodie and Pete together.

In general, $\dfrac{a}{b} + \dfrac{c}{b} = \dfrac{a+c}{b}$. In other words, when the denominators are the same and you are adding, you add the numerators together and then keep the same denominator.

In the next problem, the fractions do not have the same denominator. While having the same denominators isn't necessary for addition or subtraction of fractions, it certainly makes things easier. Finding a common denominator doesn't change the value or the amount of a fraction, it just makes it easier to work with when solving a problem. We'll take a little detour and talk about rewriting fractions with different denominators.

Rewriting a Fraction with a Different Denominator

The process of rewriting a fraction with a different denominator is helpful to know. Here is an example to show you how it works.

We'll start with a fraction that is probably pretty familiar to you, ½. Think about how to represent half of the amount if you have a whole divided into 4 equal parts—half would be 2, or 1/4. If the whole is divided into 8 parts, half would be 4, or 4/8, and if the whole is divided into 20 parts, then half would be 10, or 10/20.

So $\dfrac{1}{2} = \dfrac{2}{4} = \dfrac{4}{8} = \dfrac{10}{20}$. All of these are different ways to write the same amount. Notice that when rewriting ½ = 2/4, you multiplied the numerator and the denominator by the same number, 2. For most people, they think of the problem as $\frac{1}{2}=\frac{?}{4}$. In order to find the value of the "?" without changing the amount represented by the fraction, you would ask what number you would multiply to go from 2 to 4 in the denominator and then multiply by that same number in the numerator, so you would go from 1 to 1 × 2, or 2. If you calculate the equivalent fraction in this way, you are actually multiplying by 1 (2/2), which doesn't change the amount you have since multiplying by 1 keeps the amount the same.

Here you have it: $\frac{1}{2}=\frac{1x2}{2x2}=\frac{2}{4}$. To change to a different denominator, just change the number you multiply by on the top and the bottom of the fraction. So to rewrite ½ to eighths, you would multiply the top and bottom of the fraction by 4 and get ½ = 4/8.

This same idea can be shown with a diagram.

Here is ½:

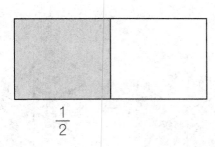

$$\frac{1}{2}$$

Now to rewrite this amount using fourths, divide the rectangle in half:

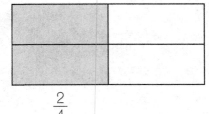

$$\frac{2}{4}$$

Notice that you have 2 parts shaded and the parts are now fourths, so 1/2 = 2/4.

EXAMPLE 4.2.2 Adding Fractions with Different Denominators

Nela and Joe are both eating the same kind of cherry pie. Nela ate ½ of her cherry pie, and Joe ate 5/6 of his cherry pie. How much pie did they eat together?

This problem is similar to example 4.2.1 in that you are adding two fractions together to find the amount eaten, but in this case, you don't have the same denominator.

The equation you would use to represent this problem is $\frac{1}{2} + \frac{5}{6} = ?$

Before we find a solution computationally, it would be helpful to draw a picture for the scenario. Here is one way to represent the situation:

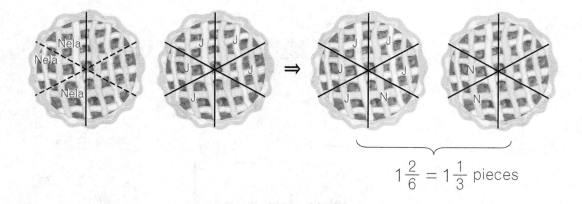

$$1\frac{2}{6} = 1\frac{1}{3} \text{ pieces}$$

Here is another way to represent the situation:

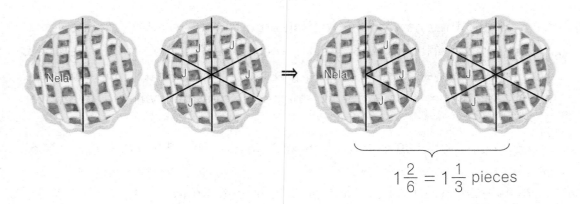

$$1\frac{2}{6} = 1\frac{1}{3} \text{ pieces}$$

Notice the answer is the same in each case; the total amount eaten by Nela and Joe altogether is 1 2/6 cherry pies. Even if you draw a picture to get to your solution, there are slightly different ways to represent the situation. This supports the idea that there is often more than one way to solve a problem.

Now that we are confident about the solution, let's do the calculation.

$$\frac{1}{2}+\frac{5}{6}=\frac{3}{6}+\frac{5}{6}=\frac{8}{6}=1\frac{2}{6} \text{ or } 1\frac{1}{3} \text{ cherry pies}$$

You could have skipped right to the calculation step without the drawing, but having the drawing reinforces the calculation. You can see that 1/2 = 3/6. You can also see that the solution

is $1\frac{2}{6}=1\frac{1}{3}$.

Solutions of Fraction Problems

How should the answer to a fraction problem be written? The answer to this question varies depending on the context of the problem. Sometimes, writing an answer as a mixed number, say 4 ½, is better than writing it as $\frac{9}{2}$, and sometimes, it doesn't matter. Sometimes, writing an answer as $\frac{2}{10}$ is fine, and sometimes, it is better to write the answer in simplest form as $\frac{1}{5}$. Converting a mixed number into its equivalent improper fraction as well as being able to write a fraction in its simplest form are great skills to add to your math tool box.

Converting a Mixed Number into an Improper Fraction

Write $3\frac{2}{5}$ as an improper fraction.

A mixed number is really an addition problem: $3+\frac{2}{5}$. So to write the mixed number as in improper fraction, rewrite the whole number part using the appropriate denominator and then add. In this case, it would be $\frac{15}{5}+\frac{2}{5}=\frac{17}{5}$. Often, students see this process as "multiply the denominator times the whole number and then add the fraction part." In this example, it would be $5\times3+2=17$, so $\frac{17}{5}$.

Converting an Improper Fraction into a Mixed Number

Write $\frac{25}{7}$ as a mixed number.

You can think of this as a division problem, with the numerator being divided by the denominator. In this case, the number of wholes is represented by the number of times 7 divides into 24 evenly, which is 3 times. The remainder is written as a fraction, so in this case, that would be 4, written as $\frac{4}{7}$. That means $\frac{25}{7}=3\frac{4}{7}$ as a mixed number.

Writing a Fraction in Simplest (Reduced) Form

Write $\frac{75}{30}$ in simplest form.

If a fraction is written in simplest form (sometimes called reducing a fraction), the fraction is an equivalent amount, only the numerator and denominator don't have any common factors. In order to write $\frac{75}{30}$ in simplest form, you would divide the numerator and denominator by the same number until there are no common factors between them. In this problem, the Greatest Common Factor between 75 and 30 is 15, and after dividing the numerator and denominator by 15, you would have $\frac{75}{30}=\frac{5}{2}$. Sometimes, you don't recognize the Greatest Common Factor right away, and then you would divide by a succession of common factors until your fraction is written in simplest form. You would get the same result if you first divided the numerator and denominator by 5 and then by 3: $\frac{75}{30}=\frac{15}{6}=\frac{5}{2}$.

There will be more opportunities to practice addition problems in the exercises. Now it's time to switch to some problems that involve finding a part, so they are more inclined to be solved using subtraction.

EXAMPLE 4.2.3 Subtracting With the same Denominator

Jenn had 3/5 of a pound of chocolate chips in her cupboard. She needs 2/5 of a pound of chocolate chips for the cake recipe she is using. What fraction of a pound of chocolate chips will she have left after baking her cake?

In this problem, you are trying to find a part, and it is an example of the Take-Away Model for subtraction. Instead of subtracting whole numbers, you are subtracting fractions. To start, each fraction has the same denominator, and you will realize it is similar to addition with common denominators. If the denominators are the same, you add—or subtract—the numerators to find a solution.

One equation for this problem is $\dfrac{3}{5} - \dfrac{2}{5} = ?$

Again, drawing a picture helps you understand the equation and the solution.

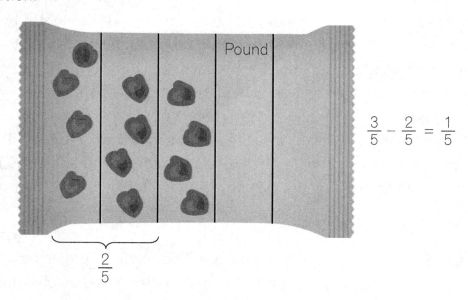

$$\frac{3}{5} - \frac{2}{5} = \frac{1}{5}$$

The solution is 1/5 of a pound of chocolate chips.

Performing the calculations for the problem: $\dfrac{3}{5} - \dfrac{2}{5} = \dfrac{3-2}{5} = \dfrac{1}{5}$ of a pound of chocolate chips.

In general, $\dfrac{a}{b} - \dfrac{c}{b} = \dfrac{a-c}{b}$. To subtract fractions with common denominators, you subtract the numerators and the answer has the same denominator.

EXAMPLE 4.2.4 Subtracting Fractions with Different Denominators

Nina had 1 1/3 yards of silver ribbon. She used ½ of a yard of ribbon to wrap a birthday present for her brother. How much silver ribbon did Nina have left after the present was wrapped?

This scenario represents either the Take-Away Model $1\dfrac{1}{3} - \dfrac{1}{2} = ?$ or the Missing Addend Model $\dfrac{1}{2} + ? = 1\dfrac{1}{3}$. In either case, you are trying to find the part, so this is a subtraction problem.

A diagram helps visualize the scenario represented in the example.

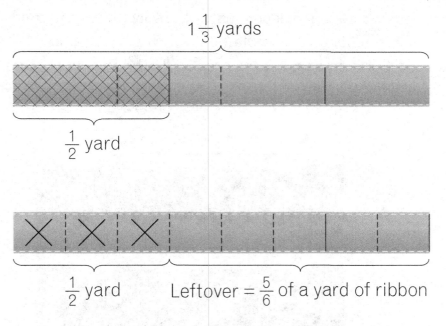

As you can see, the solution is 5/6 of a yard of ribbon left after the present is wrapped. Notice the problem is solved naturally, but converting the mixed number $1\frac{1}{3}$ to $\frac{4}{3}$ and then to $\frac{8}{6}$ makes the problem easier to solve. At the same time, the ½ can be thought of as 3/6.

The calculations used for the solution are $1\frac{1}{3}-\frac{1}{2}=\frac{4}{3}-\frac{1}{2}=\frac{8}{6}-\frac{3}{6}=\frac{5}{6}$ of a yard of ribbon left.

This example uses the Comparison Model for subtraction.

EXAMPLE 4.2.5 Subtracting Fractions with Different Denominators

Ashwin ate ¾ of his candy bar and Boris ate 2/3 of his identical candy bar. Who ate more candy, and how much more did he eat?

Without finding a common denominator, the only way to determine which person ate the most candy would be to draw out the amount eaten by Ashwin and Boris. In doing so, you realize that Ashwin ate more candy than Boris, as shown below.

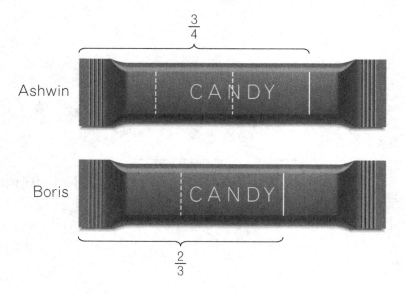

Now it is a matter of finding how much more was eaten; in other words, $\frac{3}{4} - \frac{2}{3} = ?$

Taking the same diagram from above and dividing it into twelfths, it is relatively easy to see that Ashwin ate 1/12 more than Boris.

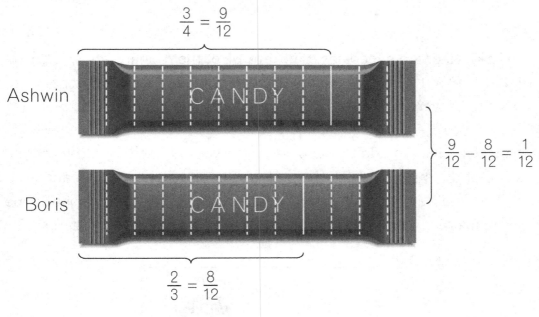

$$\frac{3}{4} = \frac{9}{12}$$

Ashwin

Boris

$$\frac{9}{12} - \frac{8}{12} = \frac{1}{12}$$

$$\frac{2}{3} = \frac{8}{12}$$

Here is a different way to represent the problem, using the same candy bar. Notice the candy bar is naturally divided into twelfths in this way. Ashwin's fraction has 9 parts, or 9/12, and Boris's has 8 parts, or 8/12. The difference is, again, 1/12 more of a candy bar eaten by Ashwin.

Ashwin $\frac{3}{4} = \frac{9}{12}$

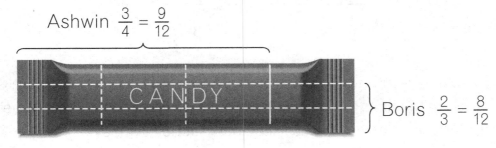

Boris $\frac{2}{3} = \frac{8}{12}$

Finally, the calculation would be $\frac{3}{4} - \frac{2}{3} = \frac{9}{12} - \frac{8}{12} = \frac{1}{12}$ more of a candy bar eaten by Ashwin.

The final example in this section is a little bit different. It uses addition of fractions but in a different way.

EXAMPLE 4.2.6 A Different Type of Addition Problem

Joe baked a batch of cookies. Sally ate 1/2 of them, Jenny ate ¼ of them, Phil ate 1/8 of them, and Joe ate 2 of them. When they were done, all of the cookies were gone. How many cookies did Joe bake?

This seems like an addition problem, and you do need to add fractions as one of the steps to solve the problem, but it has a twist because you don't have all the information given as a fraction. As with most things we're unsure about, maybe a drawing will help make things clearer.

As you can see with the drawing, Joe ate 1/8 of the batch of cookies. So now you are thinking, "Two cookies is equal to 1/8, so what is the whole?" This is similar to the problems in the first section of this chapter.

If 2 = 1/8 and you want the whole, you want 8/8, and if 2 = 1/8, then 8/8 (the whole) is 16. So Joe made 16 cookies.

Looking at this problem with a number sentence, you have $\frac{1}{2}+\frac{1}{4}+\frac{1}{8}+?=1$.

Rewriting each fraction with the same denominator gives $\frac{4}{8}+\frac{2}{8}+\frac{1}{8}+?=1$,

and doing the addition gives $\frac{7}{8}+?=1$, with the missing piece equal to 1/8. Knowing that the missing piece is the amount Joe ate means his portion of 2 cookies is 1/8, and the whole is 16 cookies.

In working through these problems, it's helpful to think of some general practices to incorporate when presenting them to your students.

1. Introduce fraction computation with story problems. This encourages students to draw diagrams, which will reinforce the calculations.

2. Connect fraction computation to whole number computation.

3. Often, informal estimation can help with a solution. Is the answer more than 1 or less than 1? More than ½ or less than ½?

4. Drill students on common fraction equivalencies.

5. **Reason before Rules!** Whenever possible, have students discover a rule through problem solving rather than being told a rule and then using it to solve a problem.

4.2 Problem Set

1. Katherine has 1/8 of a cherry pie for lunch and ¼ of the same pie for dinner. What fraction of the pie did Katherine eat? How much of the pie is left?

2. Pat bought ¾ of a pound of Granny Smith apples, ½ of a pound of Red Delicious apples, and ¾ of a pound of Honeycrisp apples at Adam's Apple Orchard. How many pounds of apples did Pat buy altogether?

3. Olivia is baking her famous Cocoa Blitz chocolate cake for a friend's birthday. She needs ¾ of a cup of cocoa for the cake and 2/3 of a cup of cocoa for the frosting. How much cocoa will she need to make her Cocoa Blitz chocolate cake?

4. Jim is mowing a large field for his friend while he's on vacation. He mows ¼ of the field on Monday and 3/8 of the field on Tuesday and will finish the mowing on Wednesday. How much of the field will he mow on Wednesday?

5. Blair jogged 1 ½ miles on Monday, 3/4 of a mile on Tuesday, and 7/8 of a mile on Wednesday. How much did Blair jog over the three days?

6. Ellery is learning a new dance routine and has set a goal to practice the routine for 2 hours each day. She practiced her dance routine for 4/5 of an hour in the morning and then for ¾ of an hour in the afternoon. How long should Ellery practice the routine in the evening to meet her goal?

7. Betty bought 3/5 of a pound of maple walnut fudge and ½ of a pound of chocolate fudge. How much fudge did Betty buy altogether?

8. Wally painted ¾ of a wall, and his partner painted 4/5 of a wall that is the same size. Who painted more of the wall? How much more?

9. Erin can knit 2/5 of an afghan in one day. If she knits for 7 days, how many afghans will she make?

10. Will biked for 2 ¼ miles, and his friend David biked for 3 1/3 miles. How much farther did David bike?

11. Crystal is sewing some new pillows for her couch. She bought 4/5 of a yard of light yellow material, 7/8 of a yard of apricot material, and 1 ¾ of a yard of deep purple material. How much material did Crystal buy for her pillows?

12. Sheila has 7/8 of a gallon of Robin's Egg Blue paint for the trim in her dining room. If she uses 2/3 of a gallon on the trim, how much of the paint is left?

13. Arline tutored some children after school. She tutored Hillary for ¾ of an hour on math, Jeff for 1 ½ hours on spelling, and Joey for 1 3/8 of an hour on reading. How many hours did Arline spend tutoring?

14. Grace has a piece of wood that measures 1 ½ feet. She saws off a piece that is 5/6 of a foot. How much of the wood does she have left?

15. Tom is a member of a CSA (Community Supported Agriculture) and has a heavy box of vegetables to tote back to his car. His share included 2 ¼ pounds of carrots, ¾ of a pound of squash, 1 pound of lettuce, 2 ½ pounds of Brussel sprouts, ½ a pound of cucumbers, and 1 7/8 pounds of tomatoes. How many pounds of food did Tom have in his share?

16. Jodie owns a restaurant and mixes up a large batch of her special Maple Balsamic Vinegar salad dressing each day. Her recipe uses 4 ½ cups of apple cider vinegar, but she only has 2 5/6 cups and doesn't want to make a special trip to the store to get more, so she decides to use red wine vinegar to make up the difference. How much red wine vinegar will she need to make the dressing?

17. Karen is training for a marathon and ran 18 miles on Saturday. She estimated that 10 2/3 miles were flat and the rest was hilly. How much of Karen's run was hilly?

18. Harold is making some furniture for his cottage. He has an 8-foot piece of cedar that he has to cut into pieces that are 2 2/3 feet, 1 ½ feet, and 3 5/6 feet. How much of the cedar is left after he cuts his pieces?

19. Dylan needs to watch 3 ½ hours of training videos before he can start his new job. He's already watched 1 5/8 hours of video. How much more video does he need to watch before he has finished his training?

20. Jill made 6 gallons of root beer and served 3 2/3 gallons at her daughter Emma's birthday party. How much root beer does Jill have left?

21. Larry has an overabundance of vegetables in his garden, and after a recent harvest, he gave ½ of the vegetables he harvested to his neighbor on the right, ¼ to his neighbor on the left, and 1/6 to his backyard neighbor. Larry then had 4 vegetables left for himself. How many vegetables did Larry harvest?

22. Karen has collected gently used tennis shoes for the past year. She plans on donating ½ of the tennis shoes to Souls 4 Soles, ¼ to ReSole International, 1/5 to Goodwill International, and the remaining 10 shoes to Planet Aid. How many shoes is Karen donating in all?

23. On a rainy Sunday recently, Ellie baked all day and had a number of cupcakes to give to her friends and family. She brought 3/8 of the cupcakes to her daughter's daycare for snack, brought 3/5 in for her coworkers, and then had 2 left to give to her neighbor. How many cupcakes did Ellie bake on Sunday?

4.2 Solutions

1. 3/8 of the cherry pie eaten, so there is 5/8 of the cherry pie left

2. 2 pounds of apples

3. 17/12 = 1 5/12 cups of cocoa

4. 5/8 of the lawn was mowed on Monday and Tuesday, so 3/8 of the lawn is left for Wednesday

5. 3 1/8 miles

6. Practiced for 1 11/20 of an hour already, so needs to still spend 9/20 of an hour (27 minutes) to meet her goal

7. 11/10 = 1 1/10 pounds of fudge

8. Wally's partner painted 1/20 more of the wall

9. 2 complete afghans and 4/5 of a third afghan

10. 1 1/12 miles farther

11. 3 17/40 yards of material

12. 5/24 of a gallon of paint

13. 3 5/8 hours tutoring

14. 2/3 of a foot

15. 8 7/8 pounds of vegetables

16. 1 2/3 cups of red wine vinegar

17. 7 1/3 hilly miles

18. The pieces total 8 feet, so all of the board is used

19. 1 7/8 hours of video left to watch

20. 2 1/3 gallons of root beer

21. 48 vegetables

22. 200 shoes

23. 80 cupcakes

Computations with Fractions: Multiplication

The goal in this section is to determine a rule, or algorithm, for multiplication of fractions. Rather than going directly to the rule, it might be helpful to make some parallels between multiplication of whole numbers and multiplication of fractions first.

EXAMPLE 4.3.1 Repeated Addition Model for Multiplication

Mary has a stack of 3 books. Each book is 1/4 inches in width. How tall is the stack of books?

This problem uses the Repeated Addition Model of multiplication. You could think of it as

¼ + 1/4 + 1/4, which would give you a height of 3/4 inches. As a multiplication problem, it would be 3(1/4) = 3/4 inches.

Drawing it out:

The answer 3/4 makes sense in the context of what each part of a fraction means. The numerator tells us how many parts, 3 × 1 = 3, and the denominator tells us what the parts are, and they are still fourths. So an answer of ¾ inches make sense on many levels.

Here's another example using mixed numbers.

EXAMPLE 4.3.2 Multiplication with Mixed Numbers

Julien has 5 jugs of root beer. Each jug has 1 1/3 gallon of root beer. How much root beer does Julien have in all?

This is another example of the Repeated Addition Model of multiplication. The equation would be $1\frac{1}{3}+1\frac{1}{3}+1\frac{1}{3}+1\frac{1}{3}+1\frac{1}{3}=5\left(1\frac{1}{3}\right)=$?

There are a number of ways to do this problem.

SOLUTION 1

One method to solve this would be to remember that $5\times1\frac{1}{3}=5\left(1+\frac{1}{3}\right)$ and then use the Distributive Property to find the solution. Multiply 5×1 and then $5\times\frac{1}{3}$ and add them together. In that case, you would have $5+\frac{5}{3}=5+\left(1+\frac{2}{3}\right)=6\frac{2}{3}$ gallons of root beer.

SOLUTION 2

This problem can be solved by rewriting the mixed number as an improper fraction and multiplying. This would mean

$$5 \times \left(1\frac{1}{3}\right) = 5 \times \frac{4}{3} = \frac{20}{3} = 6\frac{2}{3}$$ gallons of root beer.

Do you have some ideas about a rule for multiplying fractions? Let's do a couple more examples to see if your rule makes sense.

EXAMPLE 4.3.3 Multiplying Fractions

There are 12 flowers arranged in Morgan's vase. Two-thirds of them are red. How many red flowers are in Morgan's vase?

One huge help when considering multiplication problems is to realize that when you see the word "of," it means multiply. In this case, "two-thirds of them" would mean $\frac{2}{3}$ of the flowers, of which there are 12, so $\frac{2}{3}$ of 12 would translate to $\frac{2}{3} \times 12 = 8$ red flowers..

Drawing this problem out is one way to determine the answer.

As you consider the diagram, recall the problems from section 4.1 in which you are given a whole and asked to find a particular part. This problem is the same only in the context of multiplication.

The diagram shows that $\frac{2}{3} \times 12 = 8$ flowers.

EXAMPLE 4.3.4 Multiplication of Two Fractions

Your brother left you half of a cherry pie to eat for a snack. You want to save some, so you only eat 1/3 of the portion left by your brother. What fraction of the *original* pie did you eat?

In this case, you eat $\frac{1}{3}$ OF ½ the pie. Since OF means multiply, we have $\frac{1}{3} \times \frac{1}{2}$ of the pie that will be eaten.

Drawing this out, we have

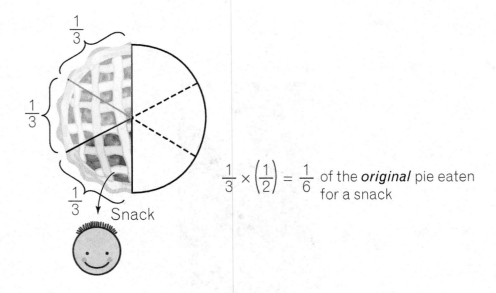

$$\frac{1}{3} \times \left(\frac{1}{2}\right) = \frac{1}{6} \text{ of the \textit{original} pie eaten for a snack}$$

You ate $\frac{1}{3} \times \frac{1}{2} = \frac{1}{6}$ of the original pie.

With each example, we're moving closer to developing an algorithm for multiplication of fractions. Here's one more example before that happens.

EXAMPLE 4.3.5 Multiplication of Fractions with the Area Model

You have a plot that measures $\frac{2}{3}$ of an acre. You mow ¾ of your plot. How much did you mow?

Think about the equation for this problem. You mow ¾ OF your plot, so ¾ of 2/3. And since "of" means multiply, the problem is $\frac{3}{4} \times \frac{2}{3}$.

This problem can be solved using the Area Model for multiplication. Recall that the Area Model tells us that the length × width of a region gives the area of the region.

In this case, we have 2/3 of an acre represented below:

Now we are going to represent ¾ of an acre on the same diagram:

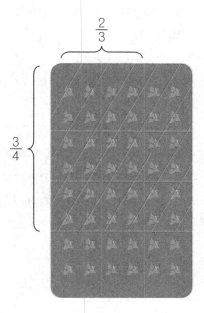

The amount that was mowed is indicated by the shaded region, whose dimensions are ¾ × 2/3. What fraction of a whole is represented in the shaded region?

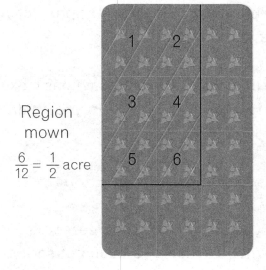

$\frac{3}{4} \times \frac{2}{3} = \frac{6}{12} = \frac{1}{2}$ an acre mowed.

Thinking back to the definition of fractions, the numerator tells you how many parts you have mown, which in this case is $2 \times 3 = 6$. The denominator tells you what each part is, and each part in this case is a twelfth, determined by dividing thirds into fourths. So the answer ¾ × 2/3 = 6/12, or ½ of an acre was mowed, makes sense from the diagram and also by analyzing the solution.

Look back at each of the examples, the multiplication equations, and the solutions and see if you can determine a rule for multiplying fractions. In each case, the answer comes from multiplying the numerators together to find the number of parts and the denominators to find what those parts are.

Multiplication of Fractions:

$$\frac{a}{b} \times \frac{c}{d} = \frac{a(c)}{b(d)}$$

In words, the algorithm says that to find the product of two fractions you multiply the "top × top" and "bottom × bottom."

Knowing the algorithm for multiplying fractions makes finding the solution more straightforward, but it is still helpful to draw out the problem to see that the solution makes sense.

EXAMPLE 4.3.6 Using the Multiplication Rule

Joey has $\frac{5}{6}$ of a pound of shrimp in the freezer. He uses $\frac{2}{3}$ of the shrimp to make gumbo. What fraction of a pound of shrimp did he use in the gumbo?

Joe uses $\frac{2}{3}$ of the shrimp, so $\frac{2}{3} \times \frac{5}{6}$ is the amount of shrimp used in the gumbo.

In this case, you would have $\frac{2}{3} \times \frac{5}{6} = \frac{2(5)}{3(6)} = \frac{10}{18} = \frac{5}{9}$ of a pound of shrimp in the gumbo.

The solution can be verified by drawing out the scenario:

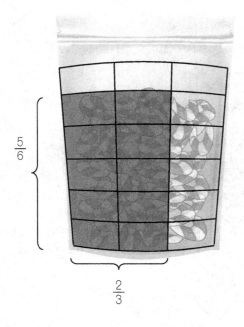

$\frac{5}{6} \cdot \frac{2}{3} = \frac{10}{18}$ of a pound of shrimp used for gumbo

Knowing how to multiply fractions is important, and it helps to keep in mind both the meaning of multiplication and the meaning of the numerator and denominator of a fraction as you compute your answer. Estimating your answer can help you stay on track. Be mindful that when multiplying by a number larger than 1, your answer is larger than when you started, but when multiplying by a number that is less than 1 (a fraction), your answer is smaller than when you started. This important concept can help you keep on track when multiplying fractions.

Let's kick things up a notch now and look at some problems that are more multi-step and a bit of a challenge.

EXAMPLE 4.3.7 Using the Correct Product

A box holds 8 chocolates. Stefan ate 2/8 of the chocolates, then Andre ate 2/3 of the remaining chocolates. What fraction of the box did Andre eat?

Before we consider a number sentence for this problem, let's draw it out.

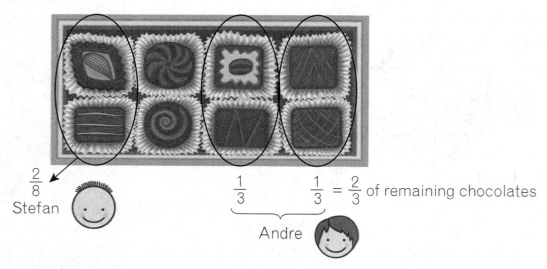

$\frac{2}{8}$
Stefan

$\frac{1}{3}$ $\frac{1}{3}$ = $\frac{2}{3}$ of remaining chocolates

Andre

Stefan ate 2/8 of the chocolates, so the portion he ate is indicated. Andre then ate 2/3 of the REMAINING chocolates, shown below.

Andre ate 4 chocolates, which is 4/8 or ½ of the box of chocolates. The key here is that Andre ate 2/3 of the REMAINING chocolates.

Now that you have an idea of the solution, let's use some equations to come up with the answer. You have to read the problem very carefully and not just multiply the two fractions in this problem together to get the solution. If you do that, you'll be wrong, so let's take this one step at a time. It will take a little longer, but you'll get the correct answer!

Andre ate 2/3 of the REMAINING chocolates, so that's what we need to find. In order to find the remaining chocolates, recall that Stefan ate 2/8 of the chocolates, or 2/8 × (8) = 16/8 = 2 chocolates, which means there are 6 chocolates remaining. Andre then ate 2/3 of the remainder, or 2/3(6) = 12/3 = 4 chocolates, which would be 4/8 or ½ of the original box of chocolates.

One more way of thinking about it is this. Andre ate 2/3 of the remaining chocolates. If Stefan ate 2/8 of the chocolates, then there was 6/8 remaining. So Andre ate 2/3 (6/8) = 12/24 = ½ of the original box of chocolates.

The key to this problem is to read it carefully and not have the knee-jerk reaction of multiplying the two fractions together. You want to multiply two fractions together, but they have to be the correct two fractions.

Here's a final example similar to the last one.

EXAMPLE 4.3.8: Multiplication of Fractions

You eat 1/8 of a pizza. The next day, you give 2/7 of the leftovers to your brother for lunch. What fraction of the original pizza did your brother eat? How much of the original pizza is left?

Drawing this problem out makes it pretty clear.

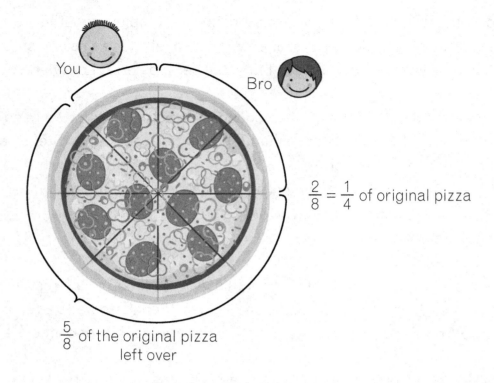

You

Bro

$$\frac{2}{8} = \frac{1}{4} \text{ of original pizza}$$

$\frac{5}{8}$ of the original pizza
left over

Your brother ate ¼ of the original pizza, and there is 5/8 of the original pizza left.

Using an equation, your brother ate 1/3 of the leftovers. The leftovers are 7/8 because you ate 1/8. So your brother ate 2/7(7/8) = 14/56 = ¼. The leftovers will be 1 − (1/8 + ¼) = 1 − (1/8 + 2/8) = 1 − 3/8 = 5/8 of the original pizza.

4.3 Problem Set

1. Helen loves jigsaw puzzles. Many of her friends have given her puzzles as gifts, or she's bought puzzles as souvenirs on her travels. Her current collection of jigsaw puzzles numbers 120. She plans on donating 2/3 of her collection to the new Senior Center in her town and then ¼ of the collection to the local library. How many jigsaw puzzles will she donate to the Senior Center? How many jigsaw puzzles will she donate to the library? How many jigsaw puzzles will Helen have left after she donates the jigsaw puzzles?

2. On Saturday, Joe and Moe went on a hike. In the morning, they hiked 7/8 of a mile. In the afternoon, they hiked ½ as far as they did in the morning. How far did they hike altogether on Saturday?

3. Rachel has 30 tulip bulbs. She wants to plant 2/3 of the bulbs in the front garden and the rest in the side garden. How many bulbs will Rachel plant in the front garden? How many bulbs will she plant in the side garden?

4. Mara teaches fourth grade and will have 32 students in her class this year. When looking at the class list before school starts, she notices that ¾ of her students have siblings that she taught in the past. How many of her students have siblings that were also taught by Mara?

5. Frank has an orchard with 18 Honeycrisp trees. If 1/6 of the Honeycrisp trees were damaged in a recent storm, how many of Frank's trees were not damaged in the storm?

6. A deluxe box of Bethany's Bon Bons has 24 pieces. Alex received a box as a birthday present, and after the first week, he had ¼ of the box left. How many Bon Bons does Alex have left?

7. Lynn has pieces of wood that measure 5/12 of a yard. If she has 8 pieces of wood and she lays them end to end, how long will it be?

8. Alec is baking cookies, and his recipe calls for 2/3 cups of butter for 3 dozen cookies. If he wants to make 12 dozen cookies for a bake sale, how much butter does he need?

9. Melissa is painting bedrooms in an apartment complex for her summer job. She needs 1 1/3 gallons of Antique White for each bedroom and is expected to paint 6 bedrooms each week. How many gallons of Antique White paint does Melissa need each week?

10. Meghan is trying to run more this summer. She has a particular route that she knows is 2 3/5 miles long. If she runs 5 days each week, how many miles does she run each week?

11. Juan is a carpenter and makes tables and chairs. He can stain one chair in ¾ of an hour. He has 8 chairs to stain. How long will it take Juan to finish staining the chairs?

12. An obstacle course goes for ¾ of a mile. If Chris has completed 2/3 of the obstacle course, how many miles has he traveled?

13. Ruth has a large garden that is 2/3 of an acre. If she wants to plant ¼ of her garden in tomatoes, what fraction of an acre will Ruth devote to tomatoes?

14. Abby has 3 ½ yards of muslin. She wants to dye 1/8 of the muslin indigo. How much indigo material will she have when she is done with the dyeing the muslin?

15. Jared bakes a batch of 18 cookies. He eats 1/3 of them for a snack. He gives ½ of the remaining cookies to his neighbor. What fraction of the original batch of cookies did he give to his neighbor? How many cookies are left for Jared?

16. Nellie has a coloring book with 20 pages. She colors 1/5 of the book in the morning and then colors ¼ of the remaining pages in the afternoon. How many pages does Nellie still have to color to complete the coloring book?

17. Skye makes ponchos and has knit 30 for her family and friends. They will be completed once she adds a contrasting color trim to each of them. On Monday, she added the trim to ½ of the ponchos, and on Tuesday, she added trim to 4/5 of the remaining ponchos. How many ponchos still need to have the trim added?

18. Jordan bought a mushroom pizza for supper and ate 1/3 of the pizza for dinner. His roommate came home from work and ate 3/4 of the remaining pizza for an evening snack. How much of the original pizza is left for Jordan to pack for lunch the next day?

4.3 Solutions

1. 80 jigsaw puzzles to the Senior Center, 30 jigsaw puzzles to the library, 10 jigsaw puzzles left

2. 21/16 = 1 5/16 of a mile

3. 20 planted in the front garden and 10 in the side garden

4. 24 of Mara's students have siblings that she's taught

5. 3 damaged trees and 15 undamaged trees

6. 6 Bon Bons are left

7. 10/3 = 3 1/3 yards of material

8. 2 2/3 cups of butter

9. 8 gallons of paint

10. 13 miles

11. 6 hours

12. ½ mile

13. 1/6 of an acre

14. 7/16 of a yard of indigo muslin

15. 1/3 of the batch (6 cookies) will go to the neighbor and 6 will be left for Jared

16. 12 pages, or 3/5 of the coloring book, will be left

17. 3 ponchos are left to trim, which is 1/10 of all the ponchos

18. 1/6 of the pizza is left for lunch

Computation with Fractions: Division

Many students are familiar with the division algorithm for fractions and can do the mathematics involved. Before presenting the algorithm, this example can help you see why the algorithm works so you can understand it. Remember, Reason before Rules!

Example 4.4.1 Division with Repeat Subtraction

Aiden has 6 pints of ice cream. If he serves 2/3 of a pint of ice cream to each guest at his party, how many guests can be served?

This is an example of the Repeat Subtraction Model for division. You know the whole (6 pints) and the size of each group (2/3 of a pint) and you want to find the number of groups (number of guests).

A diagram will help here. Draw out the 6 pints and divide each into thirds. Then remove 2 of the thirds each time to see how many guests can be served.

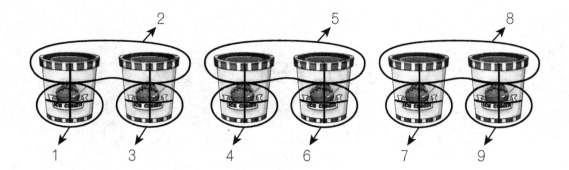

Notice in this example that after you have divided the pints into thirds, the problem becomes 18 (thirds) divided by 2 (thirds), which is 9 (thirds), 9 guests in this case.

Looking at this with a number sentence:

$$6 \div \frac{2}{3} = \frac{18}{3} \div \frac{2}{3} = \frac{18}{2} = 9$$

An example such as this can help the students understand the reasoning behind division of fractions and lead them to be more successful when dividing fractions. It shows students that there is a parallel between dividing whole numbers and dividing fractions. Division is always finding either the number of groups or the number in each group—it's only the type of numbers that define the group (sometimes whole numbers and sometimes fractions) that changes. Giving students opportunities to solve division problems without the division algorithm adds to their Math Power.

Simply knowing the division algorithm is not enough to solve the problem correctly as you still need to set the problem up properly. Having said that, it is a very helpful algorithm to know.

Division Algorithm for Fractions

$$\frac{a}{b} \div \frac{c}{d} = \frac{a}{b} \times \frac{d}{c} = \frac{a(d)}{b(c)}$$

When I was in school, I was taught that the rule for division was "multiply by the reciprocal." That worked for me, but it is a bit vague. The reciprocal of what? Past students have shared what their teachers taught them in order to remember the division algorithm, and these are much better because they tell the students exactly what to do with each term.

One teacher used "Stay-Change-Switch," as in Stay (keep the first fraction the same), Change (change the sign from division to multiplication), and Switch (write the reciprocal of the second fraction). Another teacher used the similar "Keep-Change-Flip" to help students remember the steps in the algorithm.

Here are two more examples to illustrate how division of fractions works, along with the algorithm.

Example 4.4.2 Division with the Partition Method

Pat has 1 ½ pounds of candy. He wants to share his candy with 3 friends. How much candy will each person receive?

This problem uses the Partition Model for division. You know the whole (1 ½ pounds of candy) and the number of groups (4—Pat and his 3 friends). You want to find the amount for each group.

A number sentence would be $1\frac{1}{2} \div 4 =$? Solving this using the division algorithm gives

$$1\frac{1}{2} \div 4 = \frac{3}{2} \div 4 = \frac{3}{2} \times \frac{1}{4} = \frac{3}{8}$$ of a pound of candy.

A drawing can be made to support the answer found by using the algorithm.

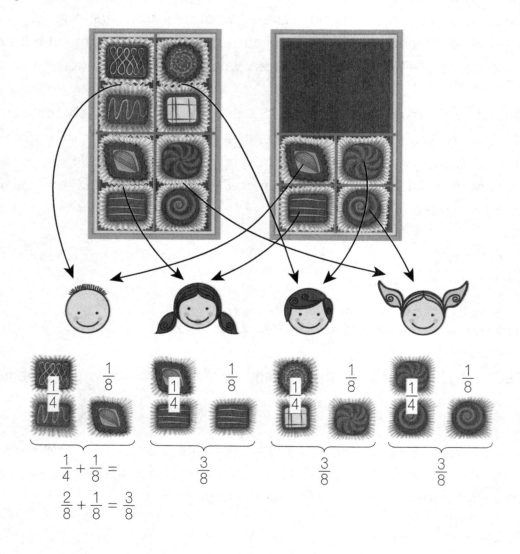

$$\frac{1}{4} + \frac{1}{8} =$$

$$\frac{2}{8} + \frac{1}{8} = \frac{3}{8}$$

Example 4.4.3 Division

Ruth has ¾ of a pound of flour. Her bread recipe calls for ½ of a pound of flour for one loaf. How many ½-pound flour portions does Ruth have?

This problem uses the Repeat Subtraction Model of division. You know the whole (3/4 of a pound of flour) and the amount in each group (1/2 of a pound of flour) and want to know how many groups there are.

A number sentence would be $\frac{3}{4} \div \frac{1}{2} = ?$

Solving this using the division algorithm gives $\frac{3}{4} \div \frac{1}{2} = \frac{3}{4} \times \frac{2}{1} = \frac{6}{4} = \frac{3}{2} = 1\frac{1}{2}$ portions of flour, which means you would have enough flour for one loaf of bread and another half loaf of bread.

This can be shown in the diagram below.

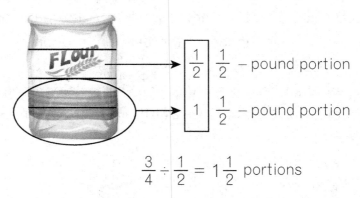

$$\frac{3}{4} \div \frac{1}{2} = 1\frac{1}{2} \text{ portions}$$

Each of the previous examples showed the division algorithm for fractions at work. The tricky part is making sure your division problem is written in the order that is appropriate for your problem. Division is not commutative, a ÷ b is not the same as b ÷ a, so you have to be careful. One thing that might help is to identify the whole in the problem and then the groups or number of groups. The whole is written first, divided by the number of groups or the amount in each group.

Remember that making a drawing for the problem can be a good first step in many cases. The drawing often helps you see which operation is best in the situation and gives you an idea of how to create a number sentence for the problem.

One last word about the traditional division algorithm for fractions and an interesting alternative that has become popular lately. This alternate approach keeps the problem as a division problem rather than changing the division problem to multiplication by the reciprocal, so it seems more true to the spirit of division.

Let's look at the number sentence for the last example with Ruth and the flour for her bread-making. We had $\frac{3}{4} \div \frac{1}{2} = ?$ Now, instead of using the traditional division algorithm, there's an alternate approach in which you find a common denominator for each fraction, then divide the numerators. Here's how it looks: $\frac{3}{4} \div \frac{1}{2} = \frac{3}{4} \div \frac{2}{4} = \frac{3}{2}$. Of course, the answer is the same! The idea here is to focus on the division once you have a common denominator. So 3 (4ths) ÷ 2 (4ths) = 3 ÷ 2 = $\frac{3}{2}$ or $1\frac{1}{2}$.

It is hard for teachers to change their way of teaching division of fractions, but I think the common denominator approach has a lot of potential and could be easier for students to understand.

Common Denominator Algorithm for Division of Fractions

$$\frac{a}{b} \div \frac{c}{b} = \frac{a}{c}$$

Division with fractions is challenging, especially since many of the answers seem counterintuitive. Remember that when you divide by a number that is less than 1 (a fraction), your answer is larger than the whole, which is the opposite from when you divide by a number that is greater than 1 and your answer is smaller than the whole. Teaching the basic operations of fractions using scenarios that have a context and can be represented by a diagram can help students enter into a problem more readily. These problems help students with the understanding that they need to solve fraction problems. The skill work is also important, but that can be accomplished with supplemental practice exercises.

4.4 Problem Set

1. Teddy has 4 brownies, and he wants to divide them equally between himself and 5 friends (a total of 6 people). What fraction of a brownie will each person receive?

2. Kym has 12 ounces of gummy bears and wants to divide them equally between 10 party bags. How many ounces will each bag receive?

3. Marty is constructing a boardwalk in a nature preserve for his Eagle Scout project. The boardwalk will measure 18 ¾ feet. He plans to work on the boardwalk for three days and would like to complete the same amount of the boardwalk each day. How much of the boardwalk should be constructed each day?

4. Kirsten has 6 cups of Chex Mix. She wants to put together some gift bags with 1 ½ cups of Chex Mix in each for her friends. How many gift bags can she make with the Chex Mix?

5. Matt has 6 cups of Chex Mix. He wants to put together some gift bags with ¾ of a cup of Chex Mix in each for his friends. How many gift bags can he make with the Chex Mix?

6. Annaliese has 4 ½ cups of Chex Mix. She wants to put together some gift bags with ¾ of a cup of Chex Mix for each of her friends. How many gift bags can she make with the Chex Mix?

7. Barton has 7 cups of Chex Mix. He wants to put together some gift bags with 2/3 of a cup of Chex Mix for each of his friends. How many gift bags can he make with the Chex Mix?

8. Don has 2/3 of a yard of material. If he divides this material into 4 equal pieces, what fraction of a yard will each piece measure?

9. Betsy made 4 ½ cups of her signature Very Vanilla Bean Ice Cream. She wants to freeze the ice cream in 3/8-cup containers. How many containers will she need?

10. Aaron made 6 ¾ cups of his Amazing Apricot Jam and will pour 1 ½ cups into each of his canning jars. How many jars will Aaron be able to fill with jam?

11. Katie has 3 ½ pounds of herb butter that she plans on dividing equally into 14 pots. How much herb butter will each pot contain?

12. Sean's soccer team has a 4 2/3-hour practice. He has divided his team into 7 squads and wants each squad to spend the same amount of time at each of the stations he's organized around the field. How much time should the squads spend at each station?

13. Tyler is redecorating his bathroom. He is going to tile ¼ of the back wall and then paint the rest in 3 equal, differently colored stripes— Aqua Blue, Sea Breeze Blue, and Mediterranean Blue. What fraction of the wall will each stripe cover?

14. D.J. has a bottle of orange extract that contains ¾ of an ounce. If he needs to put 3/8 of an ounce of orange extract in each batch of Orange Breeze Buttercream frosting, how many batches of the Orange Breeze Buttercream frosting can he make with each bottle of orange extract?

15. Skyler has a piece of birch bark that measures 2 ½ feet. He needs to divide the birch bark into pieces that are ¾ of a foot long. How many ¾-foot-long pieces are contained in the birch bark?

4.4 Solutions

1. 2/3 of a brownie

2. 1 2/10 = 1 1/5 ounces of gummy bears

3. 6 ¼ feet each day

4. 4 gift bags

5. 8 gift bags

6. 6 gift bags

7. 10 ½ gift bags, so 10 full gift bags and one bag ½ full

8. 1/6 of a yard of material

9. 12 containers

10. 4 ½ jars, so 4 full jars and 1 half-full jar

11. ¼ lb. of butter in each pot

12. 2/3 of an hour (40 minutes) at each station

13. ¼ of the wall for each stripe

14. 2 batches of frosting

15. 3 1/3 pieces, so 10 pieces and one that is 1/3 of a piece

Decimals and Decimal Computation

Facility with fractions is sometimes hard for students because there is such variety in the type of fractions available. Decimals are a specific set of fractions that have powers of 10 as denominators. This makes them easy to work with because you can easily create equivalent fractions with the different powers of 10. Additionally, decimals are a natural extension of our base 10 number system for amounts that are less than 1. The decimal point shows the change in place value from numbers that are more than 1 to numbers that are less than 1.

| 10,000 | 1000 | 100 | 10 | 1 | | $\frac{1}{10}$ | $\frac{1}{100}$ | $\frac{1}{1000}$ | $\frac{1}{10,000}$ |

The decimal 4.25 would be written as $4\frac{25}{100}$ and 0.3 is $\frac{3}{10}$, while 0.003 is $\frac{3}{1000}$. The flexibility presented with decimals occurs when looking at equivalent fraction/decimal combinations. For example, $\frac{7}{10} = \frac{70}{100} = \frac{700}{1000}$ or 0.7 = 0.70 = 0.700. As shown, adding zeros to a decimal easily changes it to a different, equivalent fraction.

Addition and Subtraction with Decimals

Addition and subtraction with decimals is similar to addition and subtraction with fractions. Generally, it is easier to add or subtract fractions with the same denominator, and in decimal terms, this would mean all the decimals are written to the same number of places. The numbers are lined up by the decimal points and then added as if they are whole numbers. The decimal point stays in the same place in the answer.

Solve $3.4 + 4.23 + 1.002$

Consider the decimals all written to the thousandths place: $3.400 + 4.230 + 1.002$

Generally, students like to write the numbers vertically with the decimal points lined up:

$$\begin{array}{r} 3.400 \\ 4.230 \\ \underline{1.002} \\ 8.632 \end{array}$$

This answer makes sense when thinking about the fractional equivalent

of $3\dfrac{4}{10} + 4\dfrac{23}{100} + 1\dfrac{2}{1000} = 3\dfrac{400}{1000} + 4\dfrac{230}{1000} + 1\dfrac{2}{1000} = 8\dfrac{632}{1000} = 8.632$

As students get more comfortable with the process of adding or subtracting decimals, they often skip the step of writing all the decimals equivalently and just make sure the numbers are lined up according to the decimal point.

EXAMPLE 4.5.1 Adding and Subtracting Decimals

Solve:

a. $34.15 + 6.023$ b. $7.32 + 18.119$ c. $35.12 - 27.9$ d. $4.156 - 0.98$

SOLUTIONS

a. 40.173 b. 25.439 c. 7.22 d. 3.176

Multiplying with Decimals

When you consider multiplying with decimals, remember that the decimals are really fractions and follow the rules of multiplication with fractions.

To multiply 0.13×0.7, recall that it is the same as $\frac{13}{100} \times \frac{7}{10} = \frac{91}{1000} = 0.091$. The denominator in a decimal multiplication problem will always be a power of 10, which makes the multiplication a bit easier. The denominator will be the sum of the powers of 10 because in multiplication you add the powers. In the problem above, the denominator is $1000 = 10^3$. Students can determine the power of 10 for the solution by adding the number of decimal places. The numerator in the problem is the product of the two numerators as whole numbers. To find the solution of a decimal multiplication problem, there are two steps—first multiply the numerators (to find the number of parts) and then "move the decimal point back from the last digit the total number of places after the decimal point," which identifies the size of the part, which is the denominator. There is a predictability and regularity in the solution when multiplying decimals, which often makes it simpler for students. It is very similar to multiplying whole numbers, with the extra step of placing the decimal correctly. Procedures such as Lattice Multiplication and Partial Products still apply. When determining the place for the decimal in the final answer, estimating the solution can be helpful, so moving the decimal point back from the last digit the total number of places after the decimal point makes sense to complete the problem correctly.

Remembering that the rules for multiplying decimals are based on the process for multiplying fractions is important. It is the same process, just streamlined because all the denominators are powers of 10.

EXAMPLE 4.5.2 Multiplying Decimals

Solve:

   a. 3.45×0.2 b. 0.005×0.83 c. 4.12×2.3 d. 3.1×5.8

   SOLUTIONS

   a. 0.69 b. 0.00415 c. 9.476 d. 17.98

Division with Decimals

Consider $15 \div 3 = 5$, and now think about $1.5 \div 3 = 0.5$, which uses the same idea but in the context of decimals. When dividing a decimal by a whole number, the numerical answer is the same as when dividing two whole numbers, but the final solution is adjusted by the number of places after the decimal point. As with multiplying decimals, this process is regulated by the underlying ideas behind dividing fractions.

EXAMPLE 4.5.3 Dividing Decimals

Solve:

a. $3.4 \div 2$ b. $0.12 \div 4$ c. $2.555 \div 5$ d. $12.12 \div 12$

SOLUTIONS

a. 1.7   b. 0.03   c. 0.511   d. 1.01

When dividing a decimal by a decimal, the conventional wisdom is to simply not do it. What I mean to say is that it's easier to work out a solution by using an equivalent problem, similar to the idea of finding common denominators to make adding or subtracting fractions easier. So if you have 2.15 (division symbol) 0.5 you would multiply each term by 10 which gives you the equivalent expression 21.5 (division symbol) 5, which is 4.3. These equivalences are relatively easy to do because of the properties of decimals.

4.5 Problem Set

1. Gary bought 1.5 pounds of ribeye steak, 3.4 pounds of sirloin strip steak, and 2.8 pounds of flank steak. What is the total amount of steak that Gary bought?

2. A snail travels 4.25 inches during one hour, 3.40 inches the second hour, and 5.15 inches the third hour. How many inches does the snail travel?

3. Hilda bought a stock valued at $42.28 per share. Her stock dropped in value by $16.78 the next day. What is the current value of the stock?

4. Laurel bought 8.6 pounds of dog food, 9.25 pounds of cat food, 3.8 pounds of gerbil food, and 4.95 pounds of birdseed. How many pounds of food did Laurel buy?

5. Jackie has decided to plant a vegetable garden in her backyard this summer. She orders 8.4 cubic feet of dirt, 6.3 cubic feet of peat moss, and 5.8 cubic feet of compost. What is the total amount of material Jackie ordered for her garden?

6. Erin's Edibles ships boxes of peanut brittle all around the world. Each box of peanut brittle weighs 12.6 ounces. Rose Murray, a regular client, orders 6 boxes each month. What is the weight on Rose's monthly peanut brittle order?

7. Gertrude is trading in her Grandma Marita's heirloom silverware for the value of the metal. She is going to use the money she receives to buy books for college. The set has 12 dinner forks, each with 1.8 ounces of silver; 12 salad forks, each with 1.6 ounces of silver; 12 teaspoons, each with 1.6 ounces of silver; 12 soup spoons, each with 2 ounces of silver; and 12 knives, each with 2.3 ounces of silver. What is the total weight of Grandma Marita's silverware set?

8. Spencer has 24 bottles of herb vinegar stored in his basement, and each weighs 10.45 ounces. How many ounces of vinegar does Spencer have stored?

9. Hayden has 32.4 pounds of fudge that he wants to divide evenly into 9 containers. How much fudge will each container receive?

10. Dana made 60.8 ounces of his special raspberry lime vinaigrette salad dressing. His salad dressing containers hold 6.4 ounces each. How many containers can Dana fill with his salad dressing?

11. Eric caught an 18-pound salmon on a recent fishing trip. He wants to divide the salmon into portions that are 0.75 pounds. How many portions will Eric have when he is done?

12. Trevor has 13.2 pounds of clothing that he is donating to Goodwill. The clothing is valued at $8.65 per pound for tax purposes. What is the value of Trevor's clothing donation?

4.5 Solutions

1. 7.7 pounds of steak

2. 12.8 inches traveled

3. The stock is valued at $25.50

4. 26.6 pounds of food

5. 20.5 cubic feet

6. 75.6 pounds

7. 111.6 pounds of silver

8. 250.8 ounces of vinegar

9. 3.6 pounds of fudge in each container

10. 9 full containers of vinegar and one half-full container

11. 24 portions

12. $114.18

Image Credits

Section 4.2

Copyright © by Depositphotos / Nenochka.

Copyright © by Depositphotos / Nenochka.

Copyright © by Depositphotos / sandesh1264.

Copyright © by Depositphotos / sandesh1264.

Copyright © by Depositphotos / Alyonka_lis.

Copyright © by Depositphotos / sandesh1264.

Copyright © by Depositphotos / adamson.

Copyright © by Depositphotos / Mr.Pack.

Copyright © by Depositphotos / Mr.Pack.

Copyright © by Depositphotos / Mr.Pack.

Copyright © by Depositphotos / grgroupstock.

Section 4.3

Copyright © by Depositphotos / Prostoi58.

Copyright © by Depositphotos / Prostoi58.

Copyright © by Depositphotos / Prostoi58.

Copyright © by Depositphotos / kchungtw.

Copyright © by Depositphotos / interactimages.

Copyright © by Depositphotos / Mikhaylova.

Copyright © by Depositphotos / grgroupstock.

Copyright © by Depositphotos / grgroupstock.

Copyright © by Depositphotos / Nenochka.

Section 4.4

Copyright © by Depositphotos / blueringmedia.

Copyright © by Depositphotos / Mikhaylova.

Copyright © by Depositphotos / grgroupstock.

Copyright © by Depositphotos / blueringmedia.

"Life is 10% what happens to you and 90% how you respond to it."

—Lou Holtz

CHAPTER 5

Proportion and Percent

In this chapter, you will see how percents, decimals, and fractions can be used interchangeably to make a problem easier. The three basic types of percent problems will be presented and used as a foundation to explore more complicated situations involving percentages. Proportion will also be presented as a problem solving tool.

Math Power Goals:

- Learn the percent, decimal, and fraction equivalencies.
- Understand the structure of common percent problems.
- Move from basic percent problems to multi-step applications of percents.
- Set up and solve porportions.

Percent, Decimals, and Fractions

In many math books, there is a fraction chapter, then a decimal chapter, then a percent chapter. There is nothing wrong with that; in fact, that is how this book is organized. The problem is when teachers think of those three topics—fractions, decimals, and percents—as entities that don't have a relationship with each other. One trend I've noticed over the years, and very much support, is to give students flexibility between the topics. When working with whole numbers, having students use the operation that makes the most sense to them in a math problem helps them generate more Math Power and adds to their understanding. In the same way, giving students the option to use a fraction instead of a percent in a problem might make it more accessible to them and result in a more positive experience.

The first step is to help students see the relationships between certain common fractions, decimals, and percents. We'll do this in chunks and then show the information in a table at the end of the section.

It's smart to start with ½, ¼, and ¾ because those fractions are familiar to most students. There are also some nice connections that can be made along the way.

$\frac{1}{2} = 0.50$, which would be 50%

$\frac{1}{4} = 0.25$, which would be 25%

In this problem, the observation is that half of $\frac{1}{2}$ is $\frac{1}{4}$, so the decimal equivalent would be half of the decimal equivalent for 0.50, which is 0.25. It also helps to point out that $\frac{1}{4}$ of a dollar is a quarter, which is worth 25 cents.

$\frac{3}{4} = 0.75$, which would be 75%

You can think of this a number of different ways. Three-fourths is 3 times 1/4, which would be 3(.25) = 0.75. It is also $\frac{1}{2} + \frac{1}{4}$, so that would be 0.50 + 0.25 = 0.75. You could also think of it as 3 quarters, which would be 75 cents, or 0.75.

Related to those above are 1/8, 2/8 = $\frac{1}{4}$, 3/8, 4/8 = $\frac{1}{2}$, 5/8, 6/8 = $\frac{3}{4}$, 7/8

1/8 = 0.125 = 12.5%

2/8 = 0.25 = 25%

3/8 = 0.375 = 37.5%

4/8 = 0.50 = 50%

5/8 = 0.625 = 62.5%

6/8 = 0.75 = 75%

7/8 = 0.875 = 87.5%

Students can look at the equivalencies many different ways here. Since 1/8 is half of ¼, you have 1/8 = ½(25%) = 12.5%. When thinking about 3/8, you can see it as 3(1/8) or 3(12.5%) = 37.5%, or you can think of 3/8 as 1/8 + 1/4, so 12.5% + 25% or 37.5%. There are lots of possibilities!

Let's move on to 1/5, 2/5, 3/5, and 4/5.

1/5 = 0.20 = 20%

2/5 = 0.40 = 40%

3/5 = 0.60 = 60%

4/5 = 0.80 = 80%

One way to think of this is to realize that if you have 5 $20 bills, you would have $100. Also, once you know 1/5 = 20%, then you can get 2, 3, or 4 fifths by taking the appropriate number times 20%.

The next chunk is 1/10, 2/10 = 1/5, 3/10, 4/10 = 2/5, 5/10 = ½, 6/10 = 3/5, 7/10, 8/10 = 4/5, and 9/10. Many of these are equivalences that have already been presented, but I'll include them for the sake of completeness.

1/10 = 0.10 = 10%

2/10 = 0.20 = 20%

3/10 = 0.30 = 30%

4/10 = 0.40 = 40%

$5/10 = 0.50 = 50\%$

$6/10 = 0.60 = 60\%$

$7/10 = 0.70 = 70\%$

$8/10 = 0.80 = 80\%$

$9/10 = 0.90 = 90\%$

As with the other equivalencies, it is based on $1/10 = 10\%$. So for $3/10$, you would multiply $3(1/10) = 3(10\%) = 30\%$. Thinking in this way also reinforces the definition of a fraction.

The last two common equivalencies are $1/3$ and $2/3$. These involve a repeating decimal, and the percent equivalent has a fraction for the exact value, which makes them easy to remember.

$$\frac{1}{3} = 0.\overline{3} = 33\frac{1}{3}\%$$

$$\frac{2}{3} = 0.\overline{6} = 66\frac{2}{3}\%$$

Often, students use 33% for $\frac{1}{3}$ and 67% for $\frac{2}{3}$. This will give you an approximate answer, but not the exact answer. Sometimes that is fine, but it can often be problematic. Make sure your students are aware of the problems that rounding the percent can bring and give them strategies to work around those issues.

Here is a summary of all the equivalencies in order of fraction size.

Fraction	Decimal	Percent
1/20	0.05	5%
1/10 = 2/20	0.10	10%
1/8	0.125	12.5%
3/20	0.15	15%
1/5 = 2/10 = 4/20	0.20	20%
¼ = 2/8 = 5/20	0.25	25%
3/10 = 6/20	0.30	30%
1/3	0.333. . .	33 1/3 %
7/20	0.35	35%
3/8	0.375	37.5%
2/5 = 4/10 = 8/20	0.40	40%
9/20	0.45	45%
½ = 4/8 = 5/10 = 10/20	0.50	50%
11/20	0.55	55%
3/5 = 6/10 = 12/20	0.60	60%
13/20	0.65	65%
2/3	0.666. . .	67 2/3 %
5/8	0.675	67.5%
7/10 = 14/20	0.70	70%
¾ = 6/8 = 15/20	0.75	75%
4/5 = 8/10 = 16/20	0.80	80%
17/20	0.85	85%
7/8	0.875	87.5%
9/10 = 18/20	0.90	90%
19/20	0.95	95%
2/2 = 3/3 = 4/4 = 8/8 = 10/10 = 20/20 = 1	1.00	100%

Solving Percent Problems I

Percent problems are common in everyday interactions. You work with percent when you go shopping, consider your grade on a test, file your taxes, and analyze statistics for your favorite sports team. A percent is a special case of a fraction, one in which the denominator is always 100. When you think about it, percent—per "cent"—means "per 100."

Generally, a percent would be something along the lines of "60% of 200 is 120." In this case, as in most percent problems, there are three parts. The 60 is the percent, the 200 is the whole or total, and the 120 is the part or percentage. Typically, basic percent problems fall into one of three categories. You are asked to find the percentage, or part, you are asked to find the percent, or you are asked to find the whole, or total.

To solve percent problems, there are two main strategies. The most common is to use a proportion. When working with a proportion, the percent problem is set up using the idea "% over 100" and "part over whole," with the whole being the number after the "of." For our example, "60% of 200 is 120,"

we would have the proportion $\frac{60}{100} = \frac{120}{200}$. The proportion emphasizes the idea of a percent; you are given a ratio that compares one number to a whole of 100 and then use that relationship to determine what the same ratio would be given a different value of the whole, in this case 200.

Another way to think of a percent is to use the math language to create a number sentence. Our example "60% of 200 = 120" would translate to $0.60 \times 200 = 120$. In the number sentence, the percent is written in its decimal form and the word "of" is thought of as multiply.

Most students prefer using proportions, but some students use both methods and switch back and forth depending on the type of problem. It's helpful for you to know both, especially when teaching the topic, so you can make the best decision for your students.

The following are examples of the three basic percent problems.

EXAMPLE 5.2.1 Finding the Percentage

You are interested in a new TV, but the price is $600, which is a bit high for your budget. You keep an eye on the price and are rewarded when you find that the store is having a Winter Clearance and all merchandise is 30% off! How much will you save on the price of the TV? What is the sale price of the TV?

In this problem, you are given the whole ($600) and the percent (30%) and need to find the percentage (the part). In other words, 30% of 600 is what number?

Setting up a proportion, you know the percent, 30%, so that number goes over the 100. The whole, 600 (the number after the "of"), is also known, and that is on the bottom of the other ratio. The resulting proportion is $\frac{30}{100} = \frac{?}{600}$. Solving the proportion, you find the answer is 180, so you would save $180. The sale price of the TV is $600 - $180 = $420—quite a bit less!

If you use a number sentence, you would write 30% as the decimal equivalent 0.30 and then you'd have 0.30 x 600 = ?, and you would get the same answer of 180, or $180.

Looking at this problem in a different way, many people can calculate 10% easily by "moving the decimal point back one space," which for 600 would mean 60. So if 10% is 60, 30% is three times that, or 180.

Some students prefer a visual for the problem, which is represented here:

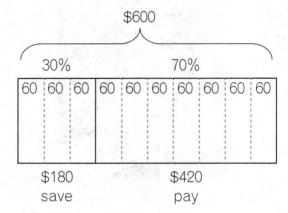

The benefit of the visual representation is that you find the amount you save and the price you pay with the same diagram.

EXAMPLE 5.2.2

You notice that 3 out of 5 statistics books on your shelf have a red cover. What percent of statistics books on your shelf have a red cover?

In this problem, you know the whole (5 books) and the part (3 books) and want to find the percent. In other words, 3 out of 5 is what percent?

Setting this up as a proportion, we don't know the percent, so that is the unknown. The whole (the number after the "of") is the 5, so the proportion is $\frac{?}{100} = \frac{3}{5}$. Solving this proportion, you find the missing value is 60, so 60% of the books are red.

This problem can also be solved using the equivalencies presented in the previous section. The fraction 3/5 is equivalent to 60%.

When faced with this type of percent problem—finding the percent— many students simply remember that you need to divide and then multiply the answer by 100 to convert it to a percent. It is fine to think this way, but also look at the proportion to add the understanding necessary in this example. Not all percent problems are this straightforward, as you will see in the next section. Understanding 3 out of 5 is 60% tells us that the proportion of red books stays the same if you have 60 red books out of 100 books.

Here is a drawing to represent the scenario with the statistics books:

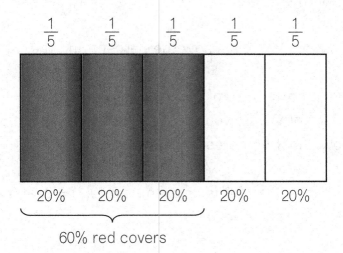

EXAMPLE 5.2.3 Finding the Whole

Your coach tells you after the game that you made 8 free throws, which was 40% of the number of free throws you shot in the game. How many free throws did you shoot in the game?

For this problem, you know the percent (40%) and the percentage (or part), the 8 free throws made, and you want to find the total number of free throws shot (the whole). This problem says 40% of what number is 8?

Setting up a proportion, you know the percent and the part but not the

whole (the number after the "of"), so you would have $\frac{40}{100} = \frac{8}{?}$. Solving the proportion gives you 20. So you shot 20 free throws and made 8 of them for a free-throw shooting percentage of 40%.

Another way of thinking of this problem is 0.40(?) = 8, and to solve this, you would take 8/.40 and get 20.

A third way to look at this problem is to reduce $\frac{40}{100}$ to $\frac{4}{10}$ and recognize that $\frac{4}{10} = \frac{8}{20}$, which would give 20 as the missing value in the proportion.

Here is a visual representation of the problem:

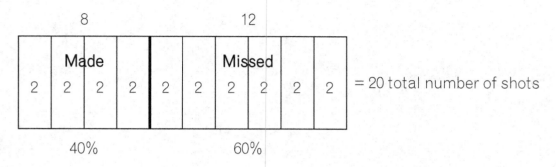

The three basic percent problems have been represented in the examples in this section. There are many situations where you need to find the percent, the percentage, or the whole, and it's helpful to be very familiar with the methods to solve each type of problem.

5.2 Problem Set

1. Harold is buying a lawn mower, and he is happy to see the model he wants is on sale at a 25% discount. If the lawn mower is originally priced at $320, how much money will Harold save on his purchase? What is the sale price of the lawn mower?

2. May has 36 lilac bushes to plant. She expects to plant 50% of them on Tuesday. How many lilac bushes will May plant on Tuesday?

3. Jill baked 5 dozen cupcakes on Saturday. She frosted 20% with lemon icing, 30% with vanilla icing, and 50% with strawberry icing. How many cupcakes did she frost with each flavor of icing?

4. Joseph is hiking a trail that is 10 miles long. He hopes to travel 40% of the trail on the first day of his hike. How many miles does Joseph expect to hike on his first day? How many miles will he have remaining on his hike after the first day?

5. Brittni bought 24 roses to put in vases around her house. She noticed that 75% of the roses were pink. How many pink roses did Brittni buy?

6. Ben caught 35 fish off the dock at Perkin's Pier. He realized that 40% of the fish were sunfish. How many sunfish did Ben catch?

7. Keith brought a large mushroom and basil pizza home for dinner. The pizza had 16 slices, and Keith ate 12.5% of the pizza that night. How many slices of the pizza does Keith have left over?

8. Sadie attempted 15 free throws at a recent basketball game. If she made 33 1/3% of her attempts, how many free throws did Sadie make in the game? How many free throws did Sadie miss?

9. Judith has 6 mocha brownies and 12 chocolate brownies. What percent of Judith's brownies are mocha brownies?

10. Shelley bought 20 flower pots at the garden store. Twelve are terracotta and 8 are white. What percent of the pots are terracotta?

11. Manon has 30 dancers in her ballet class. Twenty of her dancers need white tutus for the spring recital. What percent of the dancers will be wearing white tutus at the recital?

12. Don has flavored vinegars for sale at the local farmer's market. He has 20 bottles of raspberry vinegar, 10 bottles of tarragon vinegar, and 10 bottles of lemon vinegar. What percent of each type of vinegar does Don have for sale?

13. Drew had 10 shots in the first Catamount Cup tournament game. If 6 of his shots were goals, what percent of his shots were goals?

14. Sofia has read 54 pages out of a book that has 180 pages. What percent of the book has Sofia read?

15. A wooded plot of 45 acres has been donated to a town, with the restriction that 18 acres can be developed with trails and the rest is to remain undeveloped. What percent of the plot will remain undeveloped?

16. Betsy is painting a wall that has 120 square feet. She is going to paint 40 square feet of the wall sage green. What percent of the wall will be painted sage green?

17. The Buzas family has many pets: 4 cats, 5 dogs, and 1 goat. What percent of the Buzas family pets are cats?

18. Jason bought a box of candy and realized that 6 of the candies have nuts. If 25% of the box of candy has nuts, how many pieces of candy are in the box?

19. Ella's batting average is .350, and she's gotten on base 7 times out of all her at-bats. How many at-bats has Ella had so far this season?

20. Marti has a number of books in her library and 50% are science fiction. If she has 38 science fiction books, how many books does Marti have in her library?

21. Bethany is sewing sundresses for her Girl Scout Gold project. She has hemmed 12 of the sundresses, which is 20%. How many sundresses did Bethany sew for the project?

22. Connor is collecting sporting equipment to donate to rural towns in need. He looked over the balls that have been donated and realized that 6 of them, or 15%, are soccer balls. How many balls has Connor collected?

23. Kaity bought a new chair that was discounted 25% off the original selling price. If she saved $45, what was the original price of the chair?

24. The Distler family is on vacation, and they realized that after 2 days, they had spent 60% of their vacation budget on food and souvenirs. If they have already spent $240, how much money did they have in their vacation budget?

25. Professor Gauss has graded 16 final exams, which he realizes is 10% of the class. How many students does Professor Gauss have in his class?

5.2 Solutions

1. Save $80, the sale price is $240

2. Plant 18 bushes on Tuesday

3. 12 cupcakes with lemon icing, 18 with vanilla icing, 30 with strawberry icing

4. Hiked 4 miles the first day, so 6 miles left in the hike

5. 18 pink roses

6. 14 sunfish

7. 14 slices of pizza left

8. Made 5 shots, missed 10 shots

9. 33 1/3% mocha

10. 60% of the pots are terracotta

11. 66 2/3% will wear white tutus

12. 50% are raspberry vinegar, 25% tarragon vinegar, 25% lemon vinegar

13. 60% of Drew's shots were goals

14. 30% of the book has been read

15. 60% of the area will be undeveloped, with 40% of the area developed with trails

16. 33 1/3% of the wall is painted sage green

17. 40% of the Buzas family pets are cats

18. 24 pieces of candy in the box

19. Ella has had 20 at-bats

20. 76 books in the library

21. 60 sundresses

22. 40 balls collected so far

23. $180 is the original price of the chair

24. $400 is the vacation budget

25. 160 students in the class

Solving Percent Problems II

The previous section outlined methods to solve the basic percent problems— finding a percent, finding a percentage (part), or finding the total or whole. These three problems come up often, but even more often you will find problems that are phrased a bit differently or are a twist on the standard percent problems. These problems are more complicated, but working through them helps you gain a deeper understanding of percents and is necessary in many situations when the problems presented go beyond the basics.

We'll start with the first example from the previous section. The answer will be the same, but the approach will be a bit different.

EXAMPLE 5.3.1 Finding a Sale Price

You are interested in a new TV, but the price is $600, which is a bit high for your budget. You keep an eye on the price and are rewarded when you find that the store is having a Winter Clearance and all merchandise is 30% off! How much will you save on the price of the TV? What is the sale price of the TV?

In revisiting this problem, let's focus on the second question: "What is the sale price of the TV?" In the previous section, this problem was solved using two steps. First, the savings was calculated by finding 30% of $600, or $180. Then, this amount was subtracted from the original price of the TV, and the sale price was found to be $420.

Could the sale price of the TV have been found directly, in one step? Yes; in fact, that's how many people prefer to solve the problem. The idea here is to make sure the percent you're working with matches the characteristic you are trying to find. For this example, the amount you save is 30%, so the amount you pay (the sale price) would be 70%. So you can find the sale price directly by finding 70% of $600.

Setting up the proportion, you would have $\frac{70}{100} = \frac{?}{600}$. Solving this proportion gives you $420, which is the sale price. So the answer was found using one step instead of two.

The take-away from this problem, which will be repeated in other examples in this section, is to make sure that when doing a percent problem the percent you use matches the number used in the proportion. Sometimes the percent you need is given in the problem explicitly. If not, you may have to use the complementary percent. In this case, you would use 70% to find the price you would pay if 30% is the amount you will save.

This is a very powerful technique—thinking of the percent given and the complementary percent. Here are a few other examples to give you the idea.

If you save 10% of the original price on an item, you will pay 90% of the original price for the item. If 40% of the class passes a test, 60% of the class does not pass the test. If 25% of employees receive a bonus, then 75% of the employees do not receive the bonus. As you can see, to find the complementary percent for a given percent you subtract the given percent from 100%.

EXAMPLE 5.3.2 Finding the Original Price of An Item

You bought a coat that was on sale for 25% off the original price. If the sale price of the coat was $120, what was the original price of the coat?

In this situation, you want to find the original price of the coat, or the whole. Many students will mistakenly take 25% of 40 ($10) and then add that to $40 to get an original price of $50 for the coat. This approach is wrong because the 25% is the amount you save and $120 is the amount you paid for the coat on sale, so the values don't match.

In order to solve this problem correctly, you need to recognize that if you saved 25%, you paid 75% of the original price of the coat. So in this case, you are saying the amount you paid—$120—is 75% of the original price of the coat, and you want to find the original price of the coat (or the whole). So the proportion you would use would be $\frac{75}{100} = \frac{120}{?}$. Solving this, you would get $160 as the original price of the coat. Is this correct? Since you know the original price of the coat, you can check your work.

If the original price of the coat was $160, a savings of 25% would be a savings of $40, which would mean the sale price of the coat would be $160 - $40, or $120, which is exactly what the problem is saying! So you have solved the problem correctly.

Here is a way to diagram the problem that might also add some insight to the process:

25%		75%		
save		pay		
$40	$40	$40	$40	= $160 original price

$120

EXAMPLE 5.3.3

Misty is determining her monthly budget. She will spend 40% on rent, 25% on food, 15% on gas and travel, 10% on entertainment, 5% on clothing and the rest, $42, on miscellaneous. What is Misty's monthly income?

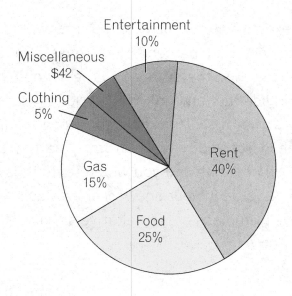

SOLUTION

This problem should have a familiar ring to it. It is the same type of problem as example 4.2.6, with Joe dividing his batch of cookies. In that problem, you worked with fractions, and in this problem, you're working with percents, but the idea is the same. You're given the percentages for all the sections except one, and in that section, you have the actual number.

If you add up all the percentages that are specifically accounted for, 40% + 25% + 15% + 10% + 5% = 95%. So there is 5% that is left for miscellaneous expenses, and you know that amount is $42. So this problem now becomes 5% of what number is $42. To solve this problem, you can set up the proportion $\frac{5}{100} = \frac{42}{?}$. The solution is 840 for the whole, so the monthly budget is $840. This problem can also be solved informally by recognizing that 5% × 20 = 100%, so to find the whole, you would multiply $42 by 20 and get the same answer, $840, as the monthly budget.

These next two examples are problems that many students solve incorrectly. Situations involving percent of increase and decrease are all solved the same way. Find the difference, the change, between the two values and then divide that amount by the <u>original</u> value to find the correct percent. If it is a percent of increase, your answer will be positive and you would note an increase of, say, 6%. If you have a percent of decrease, your answer will be negative and you would write it as a change of -6% (using the negative value in your answer) or as a decrease of 6% (using the word "decrease" in place of the negative sign).

EXAMPLE 5.3.4 Percent of Increase

Joan has a bee hive and makes honey and beeswax candles. She usually gives her products away to friends and family, but she's had such a positive response from them that she's decided to sell her products at the local farmer's market each week.

In the first week, she sold $150 worth of items, and in the second week, her sales increased to $200. What was the percent of increase in sales from the first week to the second week?

SOLUTION

This problem is a percent of increase problem. You want to find the percent of increase from $150 to $200. First, subtract 200 − 150 = 50 to get the amount of change. Then, you want to find what percent the change is of the original value, so you want to find what percent $50 is of $150 (the original value). You are finding a percent, so the proportion you would use is $\frac{50}{150} = \frac{?}{100}$, which gives 33 1/3% as the percent of increase. You can also solve this problem informally by noting that 50/150 = 1/3, which is 33 1/3%.

EXAMPLE 5.3.5 Percent of Decrease

Jeff has 20 blueberry bushes in his backyard. After an exceptionally cold winter, he noticed that only 16 of his bushes are still alive. What is the percent of decrease in the number of Jeff's blueberry bushes?

SOLUTION

This problem is a percent of decrease problem. First, find the amount of change, or decrease, by subtracting. I generally subtract the smaller number from the larger number, so I would have 20 − 16 = 4, recognizing 4 as a decrease. The next step is to calculate what percent 4 is of the original value, the 20 bushes. You are finding a percent, so you would have $\frac{4}{20} = \frac{?}{100}$, and solving this proportion gives 20%, so there would be a decrease of 20%, or you could also say the change is -20%.

This final example illustrates a situation many people perceive incorrectly. When you have multiple percentage discounts, say 25% and an additional 10%, the overall discount is not 35%. The following example shows how to find the correct overall discount when there are multiple discounts for an item.

EXAMPLE 5.3.6 Multiple Discounts

Karen needs a storage shed for her backyard and has been keeping an eye on one that seems perfect. The shed sells for $400, which is too much for Karen.

Luckily, the store is having an Anniversary Sale and all merchandise is discounted 20%. Even better, as a preferred customer, Karen gets an additional 10% off on all purchases. How much will Karen have to pay for the storage shed? Calculate the overall percent of discount Karen receives.

SOLUTION

In order to find out how much Karen will have to pay for the storage shed, we do the discounts sequentially. First, we'll find the price of the shed with the 20% discount. In order to do this, remember that a discount of 20% means you will pay 80%, so the proportion to use is

$\frac{80}{100} = \frac{?}{400}$, and the answer is $320. Then the 10% discount is applied to the $320, which would mean you'd pay 90% of $320, and the propor-

tion to use would be $\frac{90}{100} = \frac{?}{320}$, which gives you $288. So when all is said and done, Karen will pay $288 for the shed.

The next question asks for the overall discount. In other words, you will be finding the percent of decrease if an item sells for $400 and then is reduced to sell for $288. Use what you learned in example 5.3.5 to solve this problem. The difference between the two prices is $112, and you want to find out what percent $112 is of the original price of $400. The

proportion you would use is $\frac{?}{100} = \frac{112}{400}$, and the answer to this is 28, or a decrease of 28%. So a decrease of 20% followed by a decrease of 10% is equivalent to an overall decrease of 28%. The reason why this decrease is less than the sum of the two discounts is that for the second discount, you are taking a percentage of the reduced item, not the full price.

The same thing is true if you have multiple increases. A raise of 25% followed by a bonus of 10% actually gives an overall increase of 32.5%. Make up a problem so you can try it yourself and see that it's true!

5.3 Problem Set

1. Macy is practicing her dart game. For every 20 tries, she hits the inner ring 14 times. What percent of the time does Macy miss the inner ring?

2. Huang is a waiter at a seasonal restaurant. He waited on 24 tables on Saturday, and 18 of the tables ordered one of the specialty desserts. What percent of the tables that Huang served did not order a dessert?

3. Amanda is a coach for her daughter's soccer team that consists of six- and seven-year olds. The team has 15 players, and 3 of them are seven years old. What percent of the players on the soccer team are six years old?

4. You pay $120 for a lamp that is on sale for 20% off the original price. What was the original price of the lamp?

5. Frederick bought some new sneakers on sale and paid $150. The sneakers were on sale for 25% off the original price. What was the original price of the sneakers? How much money did Frederick save buying the sneakers on sale?

6. Horatio bought some new sunglasses on sale for 15% off the original price. If he paid $170 for the sunglasses, what was the original price?

7. Josie was looking for a new computer and was happy to find the one she wanted on sale! The computer was on sale for 30% off the original price and she saved $90. What was the original price of the computer? How much did Josie pay for the computer?

8. Shanice is a bridesmaid in her best friend's wedding. She needs to buy a certain type of shoe to wear with her dress and, lucky for her, they are on sale. The shoes were on sale for 40% off and she saved $40. What was the sale price of Shanice's shoes?

9. Doug's Great Dane is 12 pounds when he brings it home from the humane society. In two weeks, the dog gains 150% of his body weight! How many pounds did the dog gain? What is the dog's weight after two weeks?

10. Kelsey has been working at Champion Communications for one year, and the company has been very successful. When she was hired, her yearly salary was $32,000 with benefits, and her manager has recommended that she receive a raise of 30%. What is Kelsey's new yearly salary?

11. Sammy loves snow globes and has collected 25 of them on her travels. After a recent trip, her collection increased by 40%. How many snow globes does Sammy have in her collection now?

12. Lenny carries 8 different flavors of gelato at his scoop shop. It is proving a popular item, and he wants to increase the number of flavors by 125%. How many different gelato flavors will Lenny offer after he adds these new flavors?

13. Mrs. Jones planted 12 pepper plants last year and is planting 15 pepper plants this year. What is the percent of increase in the number of pepper plants Mrs. Jones is planting this year?

14. Marcus is an environmental science major, and for his honors project, he is studying the loon population on Lake Calhoun. In 2015, there were 10 nesting pairs of loons, and in 2016, there were 14 nesting pairs. What is the percent of increase in the number of nesting pairs from 2015 to 2016?

15. Lucy is the new manager for a cleaning company. Last year, the company averaged 20 customer complaints each month, and now, because of Lucy's changes, the number of complaints has decreased to an average of 9 complaints each month. What is the percent of decrease in the average number of complaints each month now that Lucy's come on board?

16. The number of bats overwintering in a certain cave has decreased from 100 to 95. What is the percent of decrease in the bat population in the cave?

17. In 2012, there were 50 members in the skateboarding club at Ramperville High School. In 2013, there were 40 members in the skateboarding club. What is the percent of decrease in the membership of the skateboarding club from 2012 to 2013?

18. Callum wants to start investing in the stock market and has his eyes on KSBW Electronics. During the first two days, the stock increased 20% each day, then decreased 10%. What was the overall increase or decrease of the stock over the three days?

19. The number of people downloading a certain song increased by 15%, then decreased by 20%. What is the overall increase or decrease in the number of people downloading the song over this period?

20. Narles' lawn-mowing business has been growing due to his excellent reputation. He started with 40 customers in the first week of the summer, then increased by 10%, then increased by 25%. How many customers does Narles have now, and what is the overall percent of increase in the number of customers?

21. Paris needs to buy a new couch for her apartment. The couch she is interested in costs $400. Luckily, there is a big remodeling sale going on at the local store, and they are offering a 25% discount on all furniture! And as a preferred customer, Paris gets an additional 20% off any purchases made in November. How much will Paris have to pay for her new couch?

22. You see a loveseat that would be perfect for your house, but at $400, it is too expensive, and you decide to wait and see if it will go on sale. A month or so later, the price is reduced by 20%! However, you have heard rumors about a super-closeout sale and decide to wait a bit to see what happens. Luckily, you were right: the store holds a one-day 40% off sale on already reduced items, and you rush in to get the loveseat. How much did you pay for the loveseat? What percent off the original price did you end up paying?

23. Taylor is painting a wall in her bedroom. The first day, she painted 20% of the wall. The second day, she painted 75% of the unpainted part of the wall. What percent of the entire wall does she have left to paint on the third day?

24. Stella ate 10% of the strawberry bread she brought to work during her midmorning coffee break. She ate 66 2/3% of the remainder of the strawberry bread for lunch. What percent of the strawberry bread does she have left for an afternoon snack?

25. Erin ate 25% of a cantaloupe for breakfast, then Will ate 33 1/3% of the remainder for his lunch. What percent of the cantaloupe is left to put in a fruit salad Erin is making to take to a potluck supper?

26. Eve planted 37.5% of her garden in herbs and then 60% of the remainder in corn. What percent of her garden is left to plant with pumpkins?

27. At the Sunshine Room bake sale, 25% of the items for sale were pies, 25% were breads, 25% were layer cakes, 15% were bundt cakes, and there were 6 coffee cakes. How many items were available at the bake sale?

28. Greg is inventorying a particular forest plot. He counted 35% fir trees, 29% maple trees, 26% ash trees, and 22 oak trees. How many trees were in the forest plot?

29. A farm stand sells pint containers of a variety of fruits and has 35% raspberries, 40% strawberries, 20% black raspberries, and 10 pints of blackberries. How many pints of fruit are available?

30. Brad has a collection of marbles that he is giving to his cousins. He gives 20% of the marbles to Jed, 20% to Glen, 20% to Harold, 20% to Matt, and 14 to Ed. How many marbles did Brad have in his collection?

5.3 Solutions

1. Missed the ring 30% of the time

2. 25% did not order the dessert

3. 80% of the team are six-year olds

4. Original price was $150

5. Original price was $200, so saved $50 on the sneakers

6. Sunglasses were originally $200

7. Original price of the computer was $300, you paid $210

8. Shoes were $60 on sale (originally $100)

9. Doug's dog gained 18 pounds in two weeks and now weighs 30 pounds

10. Kelsey's new salary is $41,600 per year

11. 35 snow globes

12. 18 different flavors of gelato available

13. 25% increase in the number of pepper plants

14. 40% increase in the number of nesting pairs

15. 55% decrease in complaints

16. 5% decrease in the bat population

17. 20% decrease in membership

18. Increase of 29.6%

19. Decrease of 8%

20. 55 customers now, an increase of 37.5%

21. $240 for the couch, a 40% discount overall

22. Paid $192 for the loveseat, a 52% discount overall

23. 20% of the wall is left to paint

24. 30% of the strawberry bread left for an afternoon snack

25. 50% of the cantaloupe is left for the fruit salad

26. 25% is left for pumpkins

27. There were 60 items available at the bake sale

28. There were 220 trees in the forest plot

29. There were 200 pints of fruit

30. There were 70 marbles

Ratio and Proportion

Ratio and proportion are concepts that are very helpful when making a comparison between two different entities. As we saw in the previous sections, proportions are also used to solve percent problems.

A ratio is a comparison between two numbers, a and b, with $b \neq 0$. Ratios are commonly written using words "a to b," a colon $a : b$, or in fraction form

$\frac{a}{b}$. A ratio expresses that there is a relationship between the two numbers.

EXAMPLE 5.4.1: Writing Ratios

Represent the statement "I made 15 out of 45 free throws" as a ratio.

SOLUTION

In looking at this problem, note that if you make 15 out of 45 free throws, you then also miss 30 out of 45 free throws. When creating a ratio from a statement such as the one above, there are a number of ratios possible. The key is labeling them correctly once they are created.

The ratio $\frac{15}{45} = \frac{1}{3}$ would give the ratio of free throws made to total number of free throws. The ratio $\frac{30}{45} = \frac{2}{3}$ is the ratio of free throws missed to total number of free throws. The ratio $\frac{15}{30} = \frac{1}{2}$ is the ratio of free throws made to the number of free throws missed.

Be careful when thinking about ratios as fractions. In Example 1, the first two ratios could be considered as fractions because you have an amount over a total. In the last ratio, you find the number of free throws made to the number of free throws missed, which is a perfectly good ratio but shouldn't be thought of as a fraction. You should be careful combining ratios if they are not written as fractions.

EXAMPLE 5.4.2: Combining Ratios

Ethan has 30 marbles, and the ratio of blue marbles to red marbles is 1 to 2. Noah has 25 marbles, and the ratio of blue marbles to red marbles is 2 to 3. When their collections are combined, what is the ratio of blue marbles to red marbles?

SOLUTION

The interesting thing here is that when you combine the sets together, you can't add the ratios together because they aren't given as fractions. You have to do a bit of background work to find the combined ratio of blue marbles to red marbles. Looking at Ethan's marbles, a ratio of 1 red to 2 blue means the ratio is given as a set of 3 marbles. Since Ethan has 30 marbles, you can think of 10 sets of these 3 marbles, with the ratio of red to blue marbles remaining constant. In a similar way, Noah has a ratio of 2 red to 3 blue marbles, so his ratio is given as a set of 5 marbles. Noah has 25 marbles, so you can think of his as 5 sets of those 5 marbles. Once you have the distribution of all the marbles in each of Ethan's and Noah's sets, you can add the red and blue marbles of each set together to determine a ratio of red marbles to blue marbles when Ethan and Noah combine their set.

	Ethan (30 marbles)			Noah (25 marbles)	
	RED	BLUE		RED	BLUE
Ratio:	1	2	Ratio:	2	3
Total:	10	20	Total:	10	15

Combined (55 marbles)

	RED	BLUE
Total:	20	35
Ratio:	4	7

When combined, the ratio of red marbles to blue marbles is then 4 to 7.

Problems with ratios often involve solving proportions. A proportion is a statement of equality between two ratios, often expressed as $\frac{a}{b} = \frac{c}{d}$ and true if and only if $ad = bc$. To solve proportions, students use the method of "cross multiplying" and solve the resulting equation for the missing piece of one of the ratios.

EXAMPLE 5.4.3: Proportions

At Betty's Bake Shop, you can buy 6 Snickerdoodle cookies for $10. How many Snickerdoodles can you buy for $90?

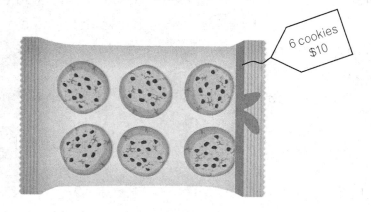

SOLUTION 1

You can solve this problem using a proportion. There are a number of ways to set up the proportion, but the main idea is that you have the two ratios matching. In other words, if in the first ratio is the number of cookies to the cost, the second ratio needs to be the number of cookies to the cost. Here is one way things could be set up:

$$\frac{6}{10} = \frac{x}{90}$$

Cross multiplying: $10x = 540$

Dividing both sides by 10: $x = 54$

So if you had $90, you would be able to buy 54 Snickerdoodle cookies. Yum, I hope you have hungry friends!

While proportions are really nice to work with, you still have to know some algebra to determine the solution. Often, when using algebra to solve a proportion problem, I usually check the answer and realize I could have found the solution without an algebraic approach.

SOLUTION 2

The known proportion is $10 for 6 Snickerdoodles and you want to know how many Snickerdoodles you can buy with $90. In this case, once you realize that you have 9 times the amount of money to spend, you can multiply the number of Snickerdoodles by 9 to get the new amount. This approach gives the same answer, 54 Snickerdoodle cookies, as when you use the proportion, but you are using parallel reasoning rather than algebra. A nonalgebraic approach helps students understand the relationships that occur when solving proportion problems and reinforces their purpose.

Problems involving fractions, such as those presented in section 4.1, can also be solved using proportions.

EXAMPLE 5.4.4:

If "X X X X X X X X X X X X" $= \dfrac{2}{3}$, how many X's would equal $\dfrac{3}{2}$?

SOLUTION

Setting up a proportion using the ratio of number of X's to fraction would give you

$$\frac{12}{\dfrac{2}{3}} = \frac{x}{\dfrac{3}{2}}$$

Cross multiplying: $\qquad \dfrac{2}{3}x = 12\left(\dfrac{2}{3}\right)$

$$\frac{2}{3}x = 18$$

Multiplying by $\frac{3}{2}$: $x = 18\left(\frac{3}{2}\right) = 27$

So you would need 27 X's for $\frac{3}{2}$.

In this case the algebraic method (using proportions) seems more complicated than reasoning out the solution. Though it's nice to have options!

EXAMPLE 5.4.5:

Your trail mix recipe calls for $2\frac{1}{2}$ cups of mixed nuts for every $1\frac{1}{2}$ cups of cranberries and 1 cup of chocolate chips. You only have 1 cup of mixed nuts but still want to make the trail mix. Using the same proportions, what amount of cranberries and chocolate chips should you use?

SOLUTION

To find the amount of cranberries needed, set up a proportion using the ratio amount of mixed nuts to amount of cranberries.

$$\frac{2.5}{1.5} = \frac{1}{x}$$

Cross Multiplying: $2.5x = 1.5$

Dividing by 2.5: $x = 0.6$

So you would need 0.6 or $\frac{3}{5}$ of a cup of cranberries for the trail mix.

In a similar way, to find the amount of chocolate chips needed, set up a proportion using the ratio amount of mixed nuts to amount of chocolate chips.

$$\frac{2.5}{1} = \frac{1}{x}$$

Cross Multiplying: $2.5x = 1$

Dividing by 2.5: $x = 0.4$ or $\frac{2}{5}$

So you would need 0.4 or $\frac{2}{5}$ of a cup of chocolate chips for the trail mix.

Learning how to solve proportion problems is a great skill that reinforces logical thinking and good problem-solving techniques, adding to your Math Power!.

5.4 Problem Set

1. The ratio of the number of free throws made to the number of free throws missed at Jenny's latest basketball game is 3 to 2. If Jenny shot 10 free throws in the game, how many did she make?

2. Gert is making floral arrangements for her parents' anniversary dinner. She wants the ratio of white flowers to nonwhite flowers to be 1 to 3. If each vase holds a dozen flowers, how many white flowers will be in each vase?

3. The Brooklyn Park City Council would like to create a committee to study storm water runoff in the city. The committee should have representation from businesses and homeowners in a ratio of 2 to 1. If there are 12 people on the committee, how many will be homeowners?

4. May looks in the window of Ben's Bakery and sees the sign "Hot Cross Buns, 3 for 51 cents." She wonders if she will get a better deal at the bakery down the street, where Hot Cross Buns are advertised at 4 for 64 cents. Where should May buy her Hot Cross Buns if she is interested in the lowest price?

5. The ratio of boys to girls in Mr. Kost's class is 2 to 3, and the ratio of boys to girls in Mrs. Read's class is 3 to 1. Mr. Kost has 30 students in his class, and Mrs. Read has 32 students in her class. What is the ratio of boys to girls when the two classes are combined?

6. The ratio of oranges to tangerines is 2 to 4 in the Citrus Surprise package. The ratio of oranges to tangerines is 5 to 1 in the Sunshine Special package. Each package holds 24 pieces of fruit. If you order one Citrus Surprise and one Sunshine Special, what is the ratio of oranges to tangerines you'll receive?

7. Suppose 10 horses need 4 acres of pasture to live comfortably. How many acres would 15 horses require to live comfortably?

8. A typical riding horse stands 15 hands (a measurement of a horse from the ground to a point between the neck and back called the withers). If a typical riding horse is 60 inches, how many inches are in a hand?

9. Jill spent $27 on gas on a recent trip to Charlesburg that was 360 miles round trip. Jill has a trip planned to Andover that will be 600 miles round trip. Assuming her gas mileage and the price of gas is the same, how much will Jill spend on gas for her trip to Andover?

10. Joe can make 2 window boxes with each piece of plywood he purchases. How many pieces of plywood will he need to build 16 window boxes?

11. It takes Mun Son 20 minutes to grade 3 research papers. If he has 45 research papers to grade, how many minutes will Mun need to grade them all?

12. Doug's hungry dogs eat 4 bags of dog food every 3 days. Doug is buying dog food for 3 weeks (21 days). How many bags should he purchase?

13. Caroline has planted a number of pepper plants in her garden this year. She predicts that each plant will yield 4.5 pounds of peppers. How many pounds of peppers should Caroline expect to harvest if she has 12 pepper plants?

14. Robin wants to make some cookies, and the recipe calls for 2/3 cup of butter, 2 cups of flour, 3/4 tsp. of salt, and 1 ½ cups of sugar for 2 dozen cookies. How much of each of the ingredients will Robin need to make 5 dozen cookies?

15. A picture measures 3 ½ inches wide by 5 inches long. If the picture is enlarged proportionally so the width is 8 ¾ inches, what is the new length of the picture?

16. Manny can clear 2/3 of an acre of land in 1 ½ days. How long will it take Manny to clear 6 acres?

17. Jane makes sparkly headbands and has sold many of them to prom goers this year. It takes 2 ½ packages of crystals for 4 headbands. How many packages of crystals will she need to make 22 headbands?

18. Georgia loves to read books! She can usually read 40 pages in one hour. Georgia bought the new book by Alex Sheppard, and it has 325 pages. How long will it take Georgia to read the book?

19. Meteorologists have found that under certain conditions, 75 cm of snow will melt to 8 cm of water. How much water is contained in 900 cm of snow?

20. A person that weighs 95 pounds on Earth will weigh 15.2 pounds on planet Metzonia. How much would Jeffrey weigh on Metzonia if he weighs 105 pounds on Earth?

5.4 Solutions

1. Made 6 free throws (missed 4 free throws)

2. 3 white flowers

3. 4 Homeowners

4. Down the street has a better buy—16 cents for each Hot Cross Bun

5. 18 boys to 13 girls

6. 7 oranges to 5 tangerines

7. 6 acres

8. 4 inches in 1 hand

9. $45 on gas

10. 8 pieces of plywood

11. 300 minutes (5 hours)

12. 28 bags of dog food

13. 54 pounds of peppers

14. 1 2/3 cup of butter, 5 cups of flour, 1 7/8 tsp. of salt, 3 ¾ cups of sugar

15. 12.5 inches long

16. 13 ½ days

17. 13 ¾ packages of crystals

18. 8 1/8 hours

19. 96 cm water

20. 16.8 pounds

Image Credits

Section 5.1

Section 5.2

Section 5.4

"Every time you subtract negative from your life, you make room for more positive."

-Anonymous

CHAPTER 6

Integers

In this chapter, the integers will be presented and strategies for addition, subtraction, multiplication, and division of integers will be explained. The relationships between the many subsets of the Real Number System will be presented.

Math Power Goals:

- Explore different ways to represent positive and negative integers.
- Be able to explain why a negative number multiplied by another negative number is a positive number.

Integer Concepts

So far, we've talked about working with whole numbers and rational numbers (fractions and decimals). There's a large part of the number line we still need to consider: the negative numbers. People living in northern climates understand below zero, and football fans see their team lose yardage during a game. Understanding how positive and negative numbers work extends the number line for children and completes the picture, so to speak.

First, here are some definitions.

Integers = { . . . , −3, −2, −1, 0, 1, 2, 3, . . . }

Positive Integers = {1, 2, 3, 4, . . . }

Negative Integers = {−1, −2, −3, −4, . . . }

Notice that the set of positive and negative integers does not include zero. If you want to include zero in your definition, you need to think of things a little differently.

Nonnegative Integers ={0, 1, 2, 3, 4, . . . }

Nonpostive Integers ={0, −1, −2, −3, −4, . . . }

To gain experience with integers, it's important to expose students to situations involving positive and negative integers as much as possible. Students already have some understanding of negative numbers from solving subtraction problems, and that makes a great foundation to start from. Here are some ways students can see positive and negative numbers at work in the classroom:

- Number lines with positive and negative integers

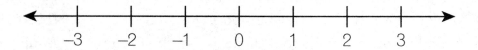

- Role play—as a store owner in which the account book has positive and negative entries or a mail carrier who delivers bills (negative numbers) and checks (positive numbers) to a house

- A football field with players gaining yards (positive numbers) and losing yards (negative numbers)

- Moving up and down the elevator in a building with a number of floors

- Red and black chips, where black chips represent positive values and red chips represent negative values

Red and black chips can be used to help students get hands-on and visual experience with positive and negative values. Teachers can use checkers or can laminate red paper on top of black paper and use a paper cutter to create square chips with black on one side and red on the other. The visual as well as the hands-on experience can help many students get comfortable with integer concepts. The operations of addition, subtraction, multiplication, and division can also be modeled using the chips.

When using red and black chips, the idea is that each black chip represents 1 (positive 1) and each red chip represents −1 (negative 1). Additionally, 1 red chip combined with 1 black chip represents 0 (zero). In other words, a red chip and a black chip cancel each other out.

EXAMPLE 6.1.1

Represent 3 using red and black chips.

SOLUTION

The easiest way to represent 3 is to just use 3 black chips as shown:

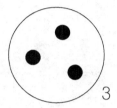

There are also other equivalent ways to show 3. These other ways use the idea that 1 red chip and 1 black chip together don't change the amount represented.

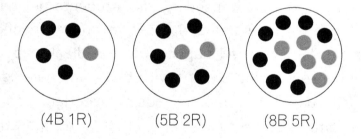

(4B 1R)   (5B 2R)   (8B 5R)

EXAMPLE 6.1.2

Represent −2 using red and black chips.

SOLUTION

As in Example 6.1.1, there are many ways to represent –2. Some examples are shown below:

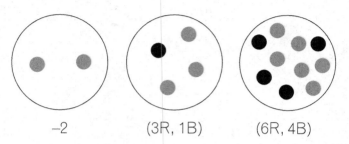

| –2 | (3R, 1B) | (6R, 4B) |

EXAMPLE 6.1.3

What integer is represented by the following red and black chips?

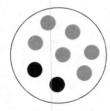

SOLUTION

At first glance, it is helpful to notice that there are more red chips than black chips, which leads one to think the integer represented will be a negative integer. To find the specific integer represented, count the number of red and black chips. There are 6 red chips and 2 black chips, which represents –4. Aligning the red and black chips in pairs helps you see that there are 4 red chips left beyond the pairs, which verifies our answer of –4.

Using red and black chips to represent positive and negative integers gives students a visual and kinesthetic experience that helps them become comfortable with this new set of numbers. The red and black chips will be used extensively in the following sections to model addition, subtraction, and multiplication of integers.

Operations with Integers: Addition and Subtraction

In keeping with the practice of previous chapters, when considering addition, subtraction, multiplication, and division of integers, the goal will continue to be "Reason before Rules." Using the red and black chips will help your students discover rules to follow when working with integers. Having experience with the operations before being given a set of rules should lead to better understanding and more success when using them in calculations.

Addition of integers

When adding integers, the models developed when using whole numbers still apply. Represent each integer using the red and black chips, then combine the two integers together and find the value represented by the combined set.

EXAMPLE 6.2.1

Evaluate each of the following:

    a. $2 + 3$ b. $-2 + (-3)$ c. $2 + (-3)$ d. $-2 + 3$

SOLUTION

a. $2 + 3 = 5$

When representing this equation using the chips,

$$2 + 3 = 2 \text{ black chips} + 3 \text{ black chips} = 5 \text{ black chips} = 5$$

This is shown below:

$2 + 3 =$

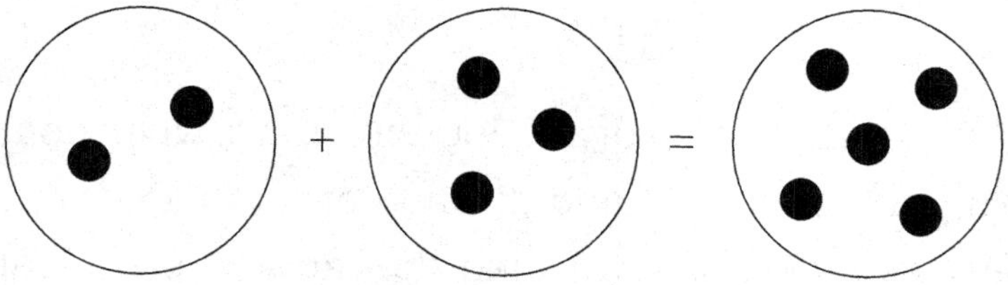

$= 5$

b. $-2 + (-3) = -5$

When representing this equation using the chips,

$$-2 + (-3) = 2 \text{ red chips} + 3 \text{ red chips} = 5 \text{ red chips} = -5$$

This is shown below:

$-2 + (-3) =$

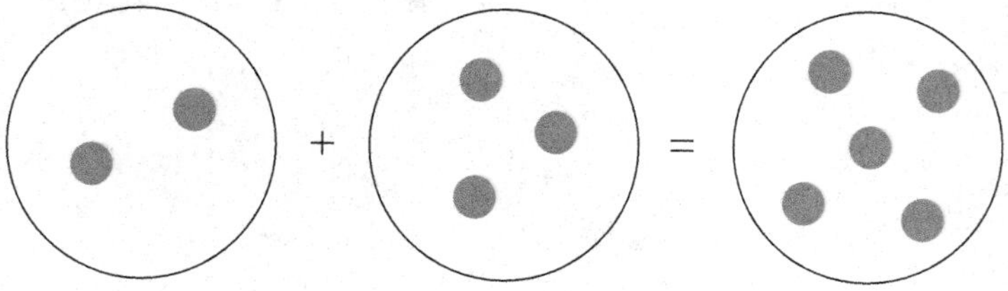

$= -5$

c. $2 + (-3) = -1$

When representing this equation using the chips,

$$2 + (-3) = 2 \text{ black chips} + 3 \text{ red chips} = 1 \text{ red chip} = -1$$

This is shown below:

d. $-2 + 3 = 1$

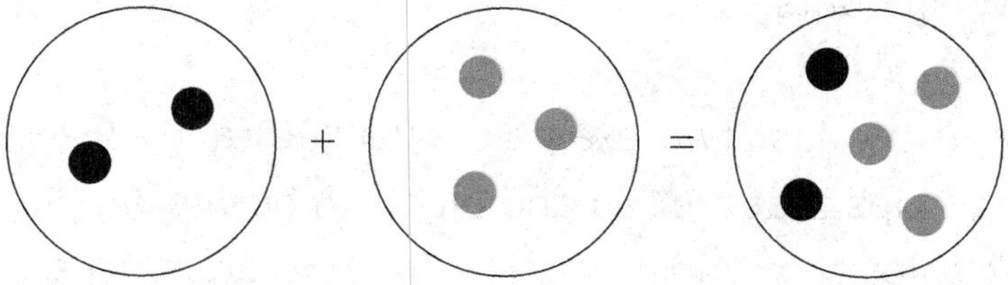

When representing this equation using chips,

$$-2 + 3 = 2 \text{ red chips} + 3 \text{ black chips} = 1 \text{ black chip} = 1$$

This is shown below:

What did you notice as you were evaluating each addition problem? Can you think of some generalities, or rules, you can apply to addition problems with positive and negative integers?

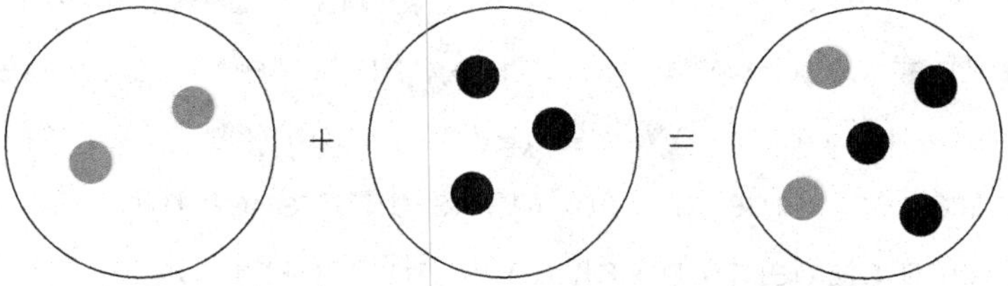

You probably realized that for the first two examples, $2 + 3$ and $-2 + (-3)$, you are adding chips of only one color and the answer has the same color. In other words, red chips + red chips = more red chips and, similarly, black chips + black chips = more black chips. This is an important observation! I like to think of it as "When the signs (colors) of the integers are the same (i.e., both positive or both negative), the answer has the same sign (color) as the integers and is the sum of the two amounts."

Now look at the last two examples, 2 + (−3) and −2 + 3, in which you are adding chips that are red and black. In both examples, you have red and black chips that cancel each other out, creating an answer that is smaller than either original amount. The answer when there are more red chips is negative, and the answer when there are more black chips is positive, and is the difference between the amounts. I think of this as "When the signs (colors) of the integers are different (i.e., one negative and one positive), the answer has the sign (color) of the larger amount and is the difference between the two amounts."

When I think about adding positive and negative integers, I like to think of it as a two-step process. The first step is to determine the sign of your answer (either positive or negative), and the second step is to determine the amount of the answer (either adding the two original values if the signs are the same or finding the difference if the signs are not the same). Having students break down the operation into two parts helps them see the importance of each step and gives them a way to start the addition problem. Ask the easier question first—"What sign will your answer have?"—then have the student either add the two amounts together or find the difference, depending on the problem, to get the final answer. One possible point of confusion for students is that they are solving an addition problem, but to find the answer, they have to find the difference, or subtract. The roles of addition and subtraction are somewhat blurred when working with integers, which can add to the dismay for students who are less confident in their math skills.

Guidelines for Adding Integers

When the signs are the same: a + b or −a + (−b)
   The answer has the same sign as the integers and is the sum of the two integers.

When the signs are different: a + (−b) or −a + b
   The answer has the same sign as the larger (in absolute value) of the two integers and is the difference between the two integers.

Subtraction of Integers

When considering subtraction of integers, most students don't subtract at all. More often, a subtraction problem "a − b" is rewritten as "a + (−b)," a process known as "adding the opposite." This is actually a great strategy because the rules for adding integers are a bit easier to follow than those for subtracting integers.

EXAMPLE 6.2.2

Use the process of "adding the opposite" to find the solution to 6 − (−4).

SOLUTION A

To solve 6 − (−4), you need to think of it as 6 black chips minus 4 red chips, since the 6 is positive and the 4 is negative. The "adding the opposite" comes in when you replace the 4 red chips for the "opposite," or 4 black chips.

$6 - (-4) =$ 6 black chips $-$ 4 red chips $=$ 6 black chips $+$ 4 black chips $=$ 10 black chips $= 10$

This is shown below:

SOLUTION B

Another way to solve this problem is to subtract using the chips. The process of subtraction with the red and black chips is interesting. The first step is to put in what you are going to take out: the "b" value. In this case, that would be the 4 red chips. The second step is to add additional chips so the amount you have is equal to the first value, the "a." In this case, you would add 10 black chips so the number 6 is represented. Once that is done, then you subtract the second number from the first, essentially removing the 4 red chips. You can see that what is left in the set is the 10 black chips, which would mean the answer is 10.

This is shown below:

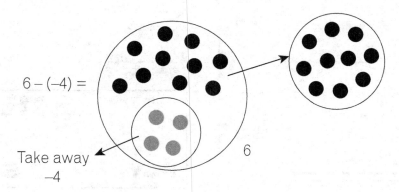

$$6 - (-4) =$$

Take away
−4

6

As you can see, subtraction with integers is not as straightforward as addition, but if you follow the steps properly, you will get the correct answer. The idea of subtraction as "adding the opposite" is a much more attractive approach.

Along with the chips, there are other ways to involve students in problems involving addition and subtraction of integers. As mentioned before, students can role–play situations where they receive a check (positive integers) or a bill (negative integers).

More Models for Addition and Subtraction of Integers

EXAMPLE 6.2.3 Bills vs. Checks

You sort through the mail on Monday and find that you have a check for $5, a check for $3, a check for $2 and a bill for $4. What is the overall total from Monday's mail?

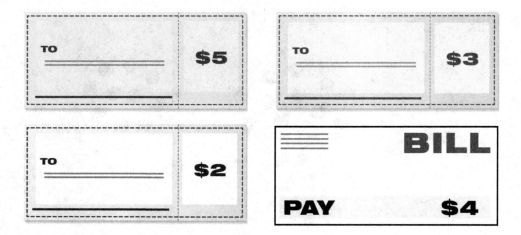

SOLUTION

This problem is equivalent to finding the sum of $5 + 3 + 2 + (-4)$, with -4 representing the bill of $4. Rather than jump to the solution of this problem, ask your students to explain whether they would expect to have a positive amount or a negative amount based on the contents of the mail. Note that the overall total will be positive because the amount of the checks in all is more than the amount of the bill, not because there are 3 checks and 1 bill. This is a subtle distinction that some students will not perceive on their own. In this case, students can add the checks together and then subtract the amount of the bill or keep a running total, whichever makes the most sense to them. The overall result of Monday's mail would be a $10 + (-4) = 6$, for an overall total of positive $6. Good for you, your business is doing well!

EXAMPLE 6.2. 4 Using a Number Line

A number line is a great way for students to work with addition of integers.

Use a number line to solve each problem.

  a. $6 + (-3)$ b. $-5 + 4$ c. $-6 + (-2)$ d. $-6 + 10$

SOLUTION

a.
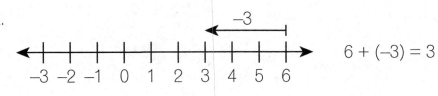
$6 + (-3) = 3$

b.
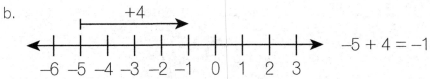
$-5 + 4 = -1$

c.
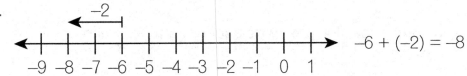
$-6 + (-2) = -8$

d.
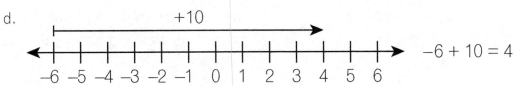
$-6 + 10 = 4$

EXAMPLE 6.2.4 Bird on a Wire

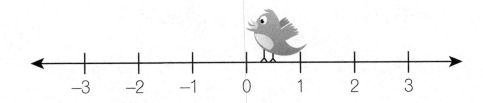

A number line works really well when working on addition problems but less well with subtraction of integers. The Bird on a Wire model is a fun way to have students work with signed numbers. It is impractical to use all the time but can be used to supplement other strategies for addition and subtraction. Having students in the class volunteer to be the bird and act out the solutions to the problems would get everyone engaged in the process.

Bird on a Wire Rules:

- The bird starts by standing on the first number in the problem.

- If the problem is an addition problem, the bird faces right. If the problem is a subtraction problem, the bird faces left.

- The bird hops along the wire according to the second number in the problem.

- If the second number is positive, hop forward that number of spaces. If the second number is negative, hop backward that number of spaces.

- The bird will land on the solution.

Use the Bird on a Wire to solve each of the following:

a. $-3 + 4$ b. $-3 - (-6)$ c. $5 + (-4)$ d. $3 - 8$

e. $-7 + 2$ f. $-6 - 1$ g. $-5 + (-2)$ h. $5 - 3$

SOLUTION

a. 1

$$-3 + 4 = 1$$

b. 3

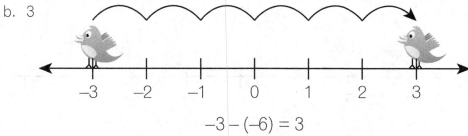

$$-3 - (-6) = 3$$

c. 1

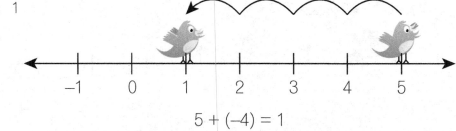

$$5 + (-4) = 1$$

d. −5

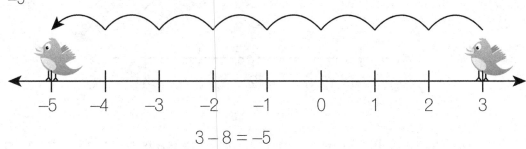

$$3 - 8 = -5$$

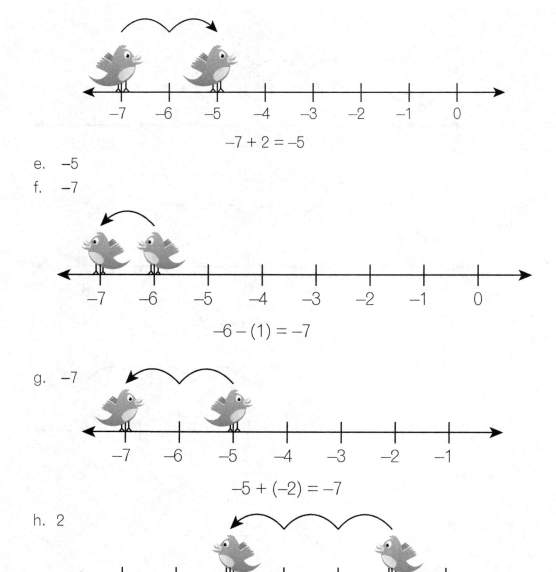

$$-7 + 2 = -5$$

e. −5

f. −7

$$-6 - (1) = -7$$

g. −7

$$-5 + (-2) = -7$$

h. 2

$$5 - 3 = 2$$

The key here is to give students multiple ways to "act out" addition and subtraction with integers. Knowing the rules for working with integers is great, but having a connection to the problem is even better.

6.2 Problem Set

Use the black chips (positive integers) and red chips (negative integers) to represent each addition problem.

1. 2 + (−8)

2. −6 + (−8)

3. −9 + 5

4. $-9 + 15$

5. $8 + (-7) + 12 + (-6)$

Use the black chips (positive integers) and red chips (negative integers) to represent each subtraction problem.

6. $5 - (-14)$

7. $-8 - 9$

8. −10 − (−3)

9. 5 − 19

10. −7 − (−11)

11. April checked her mailbox and found a check for $23, a bill for $30 and another check for $17. What is the net result of April's mail?

12. Juan went to his mailbox and received a bill for $72, a check for $121, and another bill for $88. What is the net result for Juan?

13. Will wants to buy a new bike he can ride to work. The bike costs $566. Will has been working two jobs and made $387 at one job and $285 at the other. Did Will earn enough to buy his bike? How much money does Will have left?

14. Tucker is a football player, and in the first five plays of the game, he gained 12 yards, lost 5 yards, gained 8 yards, lost 3 yards, then gained 5 yards. What is Tucker's net gain or loss on the first five plays?

15. Skyler is interested in a new stock—Nagle Neutronics—and has been watching its selling price over the past week. The stock started at $22.16 per share then lost $2.18, gained $5.40, gained $3.59, lost $1.67, and gained $2.04. What is the value of the stock at the end of the week?

16. The level of Lake Harrison is currently at 85 feet and flood stage is 100 feet. Coast Guard officials are concerned, as there is rain in the forecast. This week, the level of the lake dropped 4 feet, then gained 3 feet, gained 2 feet, gained 3 feet, and dropped 1 foot. What is the current level of the lake? How far away is the lake from flood stage?

17. The temperature on Mt. Abe on a certain winter day was −15°F. The temperature rose 9 degrees by noon. What is the temperature on Mt. Abe at noon?

18. The temperature on Mt. Philo on a certain fall day was 53°F. The temperature dropped 18 degrees by 3:00 p.m. What is the temperature on Mt. Philo at 3:00 p.m.?

19. An elevator starts on floor 12, the goes down 6 floors, up 4 floors, down 8 floors, up 5 floors, and then down 3 floors. What floor is the elevator currently on?

20. A particle starts at 0 cm, then moves 12 cm to the right, 9 cm to the left, 10 cm to the right, then 25 cm to the left. Where does the particle end?

6.2 Solutions

1. −6

2. −14

3. −4

4. 6

5. 7

6. 19

7. −17

8. −7

9. −14

10. 4

11. 23 − 30 + 17 = 10 ($10 gain)

12. −72 + 121 − 88 = −39 ($39 loss)

13. Will earned $672 and can buy the bike. He will have $106 left after his purchase.

14. $12 - 5 + 8 - 3 + 5 = 17$ (17-yard gain)

15. $22.16 - 2.18 + 5.40 + 3.59 - 1.67 + 2.04 = 29.34$, so the stock is valued at $29.34

16. $85 - 4 + 3 + 2 + 3 - 1 = 88$ feet, so 12 feet away from flood stage

17. $-15 + 9 = -6$ ($-6°F$)

18. $53 - 18 = 35$ ($35°F$)

19. $12 - 6 + 4 - 8 + 5 - 3 = 4$ (fourth floor)

20. $12 - 9 + 10 - 25 = -12$ (12 to the left of 0)

Operations on Integers: Multiplication and Division

Multiplication and division of integers is often a welcome relief for students. The rules for multiplication and division are very straightforward.

Multiplication and Division of Integers

When multiplying or dividing two integers, multiply or divide the amount (or absolute value) of the integers. Then, if the signs of the integers are the same (either both positive or both negative), your answer is positive. If the signs of the integers are different (one positive and one negative), then your answer is negative.

As when adding, there are two steps to the process of finding the answer to a multiplication or division problem with integers. First, calculate the answer from the operation (i.e., multiply or divide). Then, determine whether the answer to the problem is positive or negative to complete the solution.

EXAMPLE 6.3.1

Evaluate each expression:

a. 2(−3)   b. (−5)(−4)   c. (−4)(9)   d. 15 ÷ (−3)   e. −16 ÷ 2   f. −30 ÷ (−5)

SOLUTION

  a. −6   b. 20   c. −36   d. −5   e. −8   f. 6

This rule generalizes when you are multiplying or dividing more than two integers. When multiplying or dividing a string of numbers, you follow the two−step process as above by first finding the product or quotient. Then, to determine the sign of the answer, you count the number of negative signs. If there is an even number of negative signs, the overall answer is positive. If there is an odd number of negative signs, the overall answer is negative. This is consistent with the rule expressed above.

EXAMPLE 6.3.2

Evaluate each expression:

  a. (−3)(2)(−4)(−1)   b. (−5)(−2)(−1)(−4)(3)   c. 10 ÷ (−2)(−3)(−1)(4)(2)

SOLUTION

  a. −24   b. 120   c. −120

Now that you've reminded yourself how to multiply or divide with integers, it's time to talk about the key question. WHY does a negative number multiplied by a negative number give you a positive number? I guarantee that in a classroom of students, most of them will accept the rules for integer multiplication and division at face value and just do the math. After all, for three of the four cases, it is easy to justify the answer as you work through the rules. But there is always at least one student who asks WHY? You can answer that student with the response "that's just the way it is" or "that's how it has to be in order to make everything work out," but even as you say the words, you'd know that you should have an explanation, a way of showing this student WHY a negative number multiplied (or divided) by a negative number is a positive number.

It is a good question, but the answer takes a little work to explain. One way to help your students understand why a negative integer multiplied by a negative integer is a positive integer is to use the red and black chips. If you've been using the chips already for addition and subtraction, this is a natural way to explain this concept.

Multiplication with Red and Black Chips

Use red and black chips to multiply a × b.

The overall model that is used in this case is multiplication as Repeated Addition. There are also some ground rules. First, start with zero. Then, the "a" in a × b represents how many times you would "put in chips" if a is positive and "take out chips" if a is negative. The "b" in a × b tells you what type of chips you put in or take out—black chips if b is positive or red chips if b is negative.

a × b

1. Start with 0.   2. Put in/Take out   "b" red/black chips   "a" times.

It looks confusing, but once you see it worked out with an example, it's not too bad.

EXAMPLE 6.3.3

Evaluate each of the following:

a. 2 × 3   b. 2 × (−3)   c. (−2) × 3   d. (−2) × (−3)

SOLUTION

a. To find the answer for 2 × 3 using the chips, you start with 0, then

   Put in 3 black chips 2 times.

   ("Put in" because the 2 is positive, black chips because the 3 is positive.)

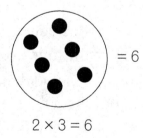

$$2 × 3 = 6$$

b. To find the answer for 2 × (−3) using chips, you start with 0, then

Put in 3 red chips 2 times.

("Put in" because 2 is positive, red chips because the 3 is negative.)

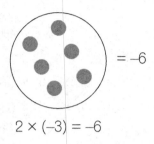

$$2 \times (-3) = -6$$

c. To find the answer for $(-2) \times 3$ using chips, you start with 0, then

Take out 3 black chips 2 times.

("Take out" because 2 is negative, black chips because 3 is positive.) This situation is a bit different because you have to remember to start with 0 and you have to put in what you're going to take out, just like you did when you were doing subtraction.

Start with 0

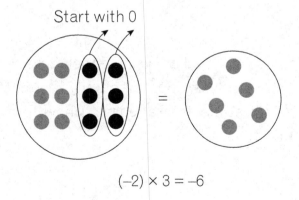

$$(-2) \times 3 = -6$$

d. To find the answer for (–2) x (–3) using chips, you start with 0, then

Take out 3 red chips 2 times.

("Take out" because 2 is negative, red chips because 3 is negative.) This situation is also one where you have to remember to start with 0 and you have to put in what you're going to take out, just like you did when you were doing subtraction.

Start with 0

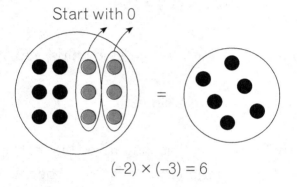

(–2) × (–3) = 6

As you can see, you get the same answer using the red and black chips as you do when you follow the rules.

If possible, have the students use the red and black chips to multiply, following the procedures outlined above, and then have the students come up with the rules themselves. That is actually the most natural way to proceed, especially if students are learning how to multiply or divide integers for the first time.

Looking at Patterns

Another way to answer the question "Why is a negative integer multiplied by a negative integer a positive integer?" is to have students look at patterns of multiplication.

EXAMPLE 6.3.4

Complete each table by following the pattern:

a.

6	X	3	=	18
6	X	2	=	12
6	X	1	=	6
6	X	0	=	0
6	X	−1	=	
6	X	−2	=	
6	X	−3	=	

b.

−4	X	3	=	−12
−4	X	2	=	−8
−4	X	1	=	−4
−4	X	0	=	0
−4	X	−1	=	
−4	X	−2	=	
−4	X	−3	=	

SOLUTION

a.

6	X	3	=	18
6	X	2	=	12
6	X	1	=	6
6	X	0	=	0
6	X	−1	=	−6
6	X	−2	=	−12
6	X	−3	=	−18

b.

−4	X	3	=	−12
−4	X	2	=	−8
−4	X	1	=	−4
−4	X	0	=	0
−4	X	−1	=	4
−4	X	−2	=	8
−4	X	−3	=	12

Looking at the patterns presented in the tables helps students see that the answer they expect from the rules also makes sense mathematically in the grand scheme of things. Everything has a reason. It's up to teachers to be able to provide as many of those reasons as possible, either by providing situations for students to come up with the answers on their own or by having some examples tucked in their back pockets that they can pull out when needed to help students see how math works.

6.3 Problem Set

Determine the answer to each multiplication or division problem.

1. $6 \times (-4)$

2. -8×5

3. $-2 \times 9 \times (-6)$

4. $5 \times (-3) \times (-2) \times (-4)$

5. $-12 \times 6 \times (-5) \times (-3) \times 4$

6. $-42 \div (-7)$

7. $95 \div (-5)$

8. $-72 \div 8$

9. $(4 \times 8) \div (-2)$

10. $(-6 \times 8) \div (5 - 8)$

11. $(2 \times 8 \times 10) \div (-8 \div 4)$

12. $(-3 \times 5) + (6 - 9) - (2 \times (-4))$

13. $(6 \times (-2) \times 5) \div (-3 \times 4)$

14. $-5 \times (2 \times 6) \div (3 - 5)$

15. $(8 \times (-8)) \times (-2 + 4) \div (-5 - (-3))$

6.3 Solutions

1. −24

2. −40

3. 108

4. −120

5. −4320

6. 6

7. −19

8. −9

9. −16

10. 16

11. −80

12. −10

13. 5

14. 30

15. 64

The Real Number System

Through this course, you've been able to explore the basic arithmetic operations of addition, subtraction, multiplication, and division with many different types of numbers. The emphasis has been on understanding the meaning behind each operation in the context of the set of numbers, but also to expand your knowledge and gain multiple techniques and strategies to perform those operations yourself or to explain them to your future students.

We've explored many of the sets that make up the Real Number System, but not all. Working with exponents and radicals is generally considered beyond the context of this course and won't be included in this text. The irrational numbers, decimals that do not end or do not repeat, are also not discussed, but they are included in the Venn diagram below so you can see how they fit in.

The Real Numbers start with the natural or counting numbers and grow from there until the entire number line is represented. Adding 0 to the natural numbers give you the whole numbers. If you add the negative values to the whole numbers, you have the integers. Then fill in the gaps with the rational numbers, which are numbers that can be written as a ratio of $\frac{a}{b}$ with a an integer and b a nonzero integer. Most people think of fractions when they think of rational numbers, but actually, it is any decimal that ends or repeats. Then there are the irrational numbers, which are numbers that cannot be represented by a decimal that ends or repeats. The union of the rational numbers and the irrational numbers is the Real Numbers. Every point on a number line corresponds to a Real Number (either rational or irrational), and every Real Number corresponds to a point on the number line.

To expand on what was written above, start with the natural or counting numbers.

$$N = \{1, 2, 3, \ldots\}$$

This set is where your mathematical education starts, counting 1, 2, 3, etc.

Then add 0, and you have the whole numbers.

$$W = \{0, 1, 2, 3, \ldots\}$$

The whole numbers are where one's more formal mathematical education starts. The inclusion of 0 expands the mathematical operations that are possible.

Now add the negatives of the whole numbers, and you have the integers. You would expect the integers to be represented by "I," but they are represented by "Z" for the German word for counting, "*zählen*."

$$Z = \{\ldots, -3, -2, -1, 0, 1, 2, 3, \ldots\}$$

Next, fill in the blanks between the numbers with the rational numbers.

$$Q = \{\frac{a}{b} \mid a \in Z, b \in Z, b \neq 0\}$$

As mentioned before, the rational numbers are decimals that terminate or repeat. A fraction such as $\frac{3}{20} = 0.15$ is a terminating decimal. A fraction such as $\frac{4}{11} = 0.\overline{36} = 0.363636...$ is a repeating decimal. The irrational numbers are decimals that do not end or do not repeat. The first irrational number most students encounter is π. Radical numbers that cannot be simplified, such as $\sqrt{7}$, are also irrational numbers. You can also make up your own irrational number by creating a decimal with a pattern such as 0.15115111511115. . . that continues infinitely but doesn't repeat. The irrational number e plays an important role in many calculations involving exponential growth.

Finally, the Real Numbers are the union of the rational and irrational numbers. Every Real Number is either rational or irrational.

$R = \{\text{Real Numbers}\}$

In order to give you a visual perspective of how all the different sets work together, here is a Venn diagram of the Real Number System:

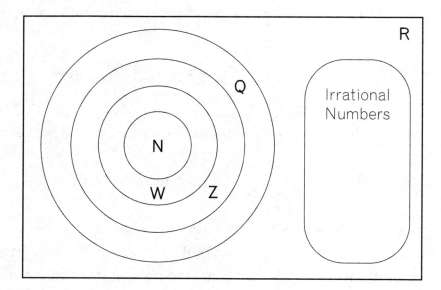

The Venn diagram helps you see that many of the sets are subsets of larger sets, starting with the natural numbers and ending with the Real Numbers. The Venn diagram shows how numbers are included in many different sets. For example, the number 2 is a natural number, whole number, integer (it can be written as $\frac{2}{1}$), and real number. The number −6 is an integer and a real number. The number 0.14 is a rational number and a Real Number. The number 0 is a whole number, integer, rational number, and real number. The number $\sqrt{13}$ is an irrational number and a real number.

The Real Numbers are an intricate set of numbers with many properties. Creating and having a good understanding of the Real Numbers is the basis of your own Math Power!

6.4 Problem Set

1. Give an example of an integer that is not a whole number.

2. Give an example of a whole number that is not a natural number.

3. Give an example of a rational number that is not a whole number.

4. Give an example of a rational number that is not an integer.

5. Give an example of an irrational number.

6. Consider the Real Number −7. List all the sets that contain −7.

7. Consider the Real Number 4. List all the sets that contain 4.

8. Consider the Real Number 0.25. List all the sets that contain 0.25.

9. Consider the Real Number −1/3. List all the sets that contain −1/3.

10. Consider the Real Number $\sqrt{7}$. List all the sets that contain $\sqrt{7}$.

11. What additional Real Number(s) are added to the set of natural numbers to obtain the whole numbers?

12. What additional Real Numbers are added to the set of whole numbers to obtain the set of integers?

6.4 Solutions

1. -7, for example

2. 0

3. 2/3, $-1/6$, 0.35, $-8/1$, for example

4. 7/11, -0.54

5. $\sqrt{19}$, 0.242442444 . . . , for example

6. Integers, Rational Numbers, Real Numbers

7. Natural Numbers, Whole Numbers, Integers, Rational Numbers, Real Numbers

8. Rational Numbers, Real Numbers

9. Rational Numbers, Real Numbers

10. Irrational Numbers, Real Numbers

11. 0 is added

12. The negative integers $\{-1, -2, -3, -4, \ldots\}$ are added

Image Credits

"The most important single element in problem solving is the individual working on the problem. The secret of real success is the confidence and desire to succeed. One must try and try again, vary the methods and procedures, have brains and good luck. There are no infallible rules for solving problems."

—John N. Fujii

CHAPTER 7

Problem Solving Revisited

This chapter brings together all the concepts presented in the book in the form of problem solving.

Math Power Goals
- Gain flexibility and further understanding in whole numbers, fractions, percent, decimals, and integers.
- Combine math skills through problem solving.

Problem Solving Revisited

This last section is an opportunity for you to look at problem solving again, only now with a renewed sense of the many possible ways math problems can be presented and solved. It may seem that you'll never master problem solving, and that is OK. The point is to keep trying. You'll get better and more confident with every problem you solve successfully! Most mathematicians have a problem or many problems they are working on at any point in time. Once one problem is solved, there is often another to take its place. The point is that there will always be problems to solve, and you should enjoy and embrace that reality!

Example 7.1.1 Dividing a Square

A square is drawn measuring 9 inches on each side, with horizontal and vertical segments dividing the square into four rectangles, as shown.

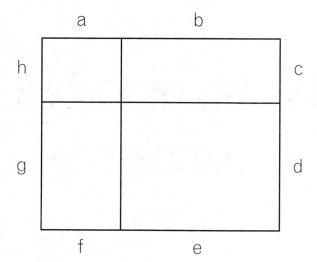

If the areas of the rectangles are 12, 24, 15, and 30 square inches, find the lengths of a, b, c, d, e, f, g, and h.

SOLUTION

To solve this problem, you need to know that the area of a rectangle is length x width. The method to solve the problem might be to use trial and error and a little juggling. Knowing the smallest rectangle has an area of 12 square inches and that the length and width of the sides has to be less than 9 inches means a and h will be either 3 and 4 or 2 and 6. Try one and see what happens. Then adjust accordingly.

The answer is given below:

	3	6	
4	12	24	4
5	15	30	5
	3	6	

EXAMPLE 7.1.2 Hiking A Mountain

You are at the base of Mt. Champlain and want to hike up to the top to take in the view on a glorious fall day. There are 3 trails from the base to the shelter at the middle of the mountain and 2 trails from the shelter to the top of Mt. Champlain. How many different routes could you take from the base to the shelter and then to the top of the mountain?

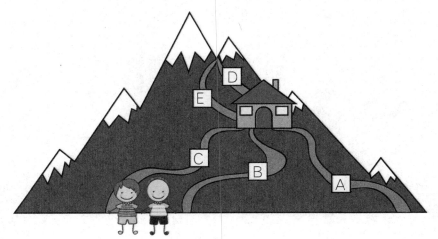

SOLUTION A

You could reason this out by thinking "How many ways can I travel from the base to the shelter?" and then "How many ways can I travel from the shelter to the top of Mt. Champlain?" The answer will be the product of the two, as this would be solved using the Cartesian Product Model for multiplication.

So $3 \times 2 = 6$ different routes from the base to the top of Mt. Champlain.

SOLUTION B

You could identify each route by a letter (as in the diagram) and then list the possible routes:

AD   AE   BD   BE   CD   CE   and realize there are 6 different routes.

SOLUTION C

You could create a chart similar to the one below:

	Base to shelter			Shelter to top	
	A	B	C	D	E
①	X			X	
②	X				X
③		X		X	
④		X			X
⑤			X	X	
⑥			X		X

6 Different routes

Problem solving is the essence of mathematics. As you learn new math ideas, definitions, properties, sets of numbers, or operations, you open up opportunities to work with these ideas in problems. And the more you practice problem solving, the better you will become. Your Math Power will continue to grow!

As you've progressed through this book, you've been presented with many mathematical ideas, some new and some already known. Having an opportunity to use any and all of the things you've learned is the best way to complete the course. Even though the course may be done, this shouldn't be the end of your education in math. Increasing your Math Power is a lifelong journey!

7.1 Last Day Reflection

Look back in section 1.1 and read your responses to the First Day Reflection prompts. Consider what you've learned about teaching math and complete the two questions.

1. What does MATH POWER mean to you?

2. What were your goals for the semester? What did you do to increase your MATH POWER?

7.1 Problem Set

1. Maya has 15 pearls. She put them in three velvet bags with an odd number of pearls in each bag. Make a table to show all the possible ways the pearls can be distributed, assuming the bags look the same on the outside (i.e., 1,1,13 and 1,13,1 and 13,1,1 are all considered the same).

2. Torrey baked some cookies. Mark took half of the cookies. Then Kenny took half of the remaining cookies. Later, Dean took half of the cookies that were left. When Torrey came home, he saw only three cookies. How many cookies did Torrey bake?

3. Solve the following number riddle: I am a positive integer. All my digits are odd. I am equal to the sum of the cubes of my digits (remember the cube of 2 is $2 \times 2 \times 2 = 8$). I am less than 300. What number am I?

4. You need to buy some flour to bake cookies and want to know the best buy based on cost: Gold Arthur, which is 64 ounces at \$4.99, or Kingbury, which is 32 ounces at \$2.30. What brand should you buy if you want the best value in terms of price?

5. For every 3-foot stack of newspapers recycled, 1 tree is saved. How many trees are saved when a stack of newspapers 100 yards high is recycled? (Note the units!)

6. I saw 20 tulips outside and 3 were red. What percent of the tulips were red?

7. Jill paid $70 for a coat that was marked 30% off the original price. What was the original price of the coat?

8. The price of a ticket to a play is $12 if bought before November 1 and $15 if bought after November 1. What is the percent of increase in the price of the ticket if you buy the ticket after November 1?

9. Travis bought a toy marked ¼ off the original price. If Travis paid $60, what was the original price of the toy?

10. There are 15 sandwiches to be shared equally among 9 people. How much will each person get?

11. You are having a party for your birthday. You buy 6 pints of ice cream. If you serve ¾ of a pint of ice cream to each guest, how many guests can be served?

12. Joey bought a chocolate cream pie. Jeff ate 3/8 of the pie for lunch. Phil ate 40% of the remaining pie for an afternoon treat. Matt ate 1/3 of the remaining pie for dessert after supper. How much pie was left for Joey to eat for his bedtime snack?

13. Jill and Linda both have $450 in their savings accounts now. They opened their accounts on the same day, at which time Jill started with twice as much money as Linda. From then on, Jill added $10 to her account each week, and Linda added $30 to her account each week. How much money did Jill deposit to open her account?

14. A math riddle: I am a three-digit, even number. My digits are consecutive numbers (like 1,2,3), and I am divisible by 12. What number am I?

15. Peter and Will each worked a different amount of days but earned the same amount of money. Peter earned $20 a day, while Will earned $30 a day. Peter worked 5 more days than Will. How many days did Will work?

16. Use four 4's and the operations of addition, subtraction, multiplication, division, and exponents to create a mathematical expression for each of the following. Clever use of parentheses can help, too!

For example, to get 8, you could write $(4 \times 4) - (4 + 4)$

$36 =$ _____

$32 =$ _____

$6 =$ _____

17. You make $16 per hour as baker at Sweetie Pie's Cupcake Shop. Because of your great work ethic and enthusiasm for your job, you've been promoted to manager, and your hourly salary will be 150% higher! What is your new hourly salary?

18. Casey bought a box of 25 homemade candies (caramels and almond clusters) at the Meadow Lake School Bake Sale. Caramels are $0.75 each and almond clusters are $0.50, and the box was priced at $16.25. How many caramels and how many almond clusters were in the box?

19. Last night in her basketball game, Brittni made 6 out of 10 free throws she shot. Today, she made 12 out of 15 free throws. What is the percent of increase or decrease in the percent of free throws Brittni made?

20. Karla's book is 75% text, 15% problem sets, 1/20 tests, and 18 pages of miscellaneous information. How many pages are in Karla's book?

7.1 Solutions

1. 13, 1, 1   11, 1, 3   9, 1, 5   9, 3, 3   7, 1, 7   7, 3, 5   5, 5, 5

2. 24 cookies

3. 153

4. Gold Arthur is .077 cents/ounce and Kingbury is .071 cents/ounce, so Kingbury is the best buy

5. 100 yards is 300 feet, so 100 trees are saved

6. 15%

7. $100

8. 25% increase

9. $80

10. 1 2/3 sandwich each

11. 8 servings

12. ¼ or 25% of the pie is left for Joey

13. $360 was deposited by Jill

14. 456

15. Will worked 10 days

16. $36 = 4 + 4(4 + 4)$, $32 = (4 \times 4) + (4 \times 4)$, $6 = \dfrac{4+4}{4} + 4$

17. $40/hour is the new rate

18. 15 caramels and 10 almond clusters

19. There is a 33 1/3% increase in the free-throw percentage

20. 360 pages in Karla's book

Image Credits

CPSIA information can be obtained
at www.ICGtesting.com
Printed in the USA
FSOW03n1601131217
42356FS